Can't Catch Me!

Can't Catch Me!

Deirdre Burton and Tom Davis

Strange Shadows

Strange Shadows
128d Oxford Road
Birmingham

Published by Strange Shadows 2008
www.strangeshadows.co.uk
Copyright © Strange Shadows 2008

ISBN 978-0-9558831-0-1

Deirdre Burton and Tom Davis assert the moral right
to be identified as authors of this work.

This novel is a work of fiction.

Printed and bound by Lulu (001)

for Dorothy and Wilfred Davis
cor unum vita una

Acknowledgements

Our thanks to Moving Hands Theatre, whose inventive show "The Gingerbread Pig" initiated a creative train of thought and our own, very different, use of the phrase. Their work, which we highly recommend, can be seen at www.movinghands.org.

Sincere thanks to friends who read earlier drafts and contributed corrections: Charlie Cattrall, Amanda Grist, Jacqueline O'Hanlon, and Simon Romer. Special thanks to Jonathan Holmes for his active support and encouragement.

October 2003

Hattie: email

Long distance glimpse

Hey Charlie—just a quick note to say how absolutely magical and wonderful it was to catch that long distance glimpse of you yesterday—hope you had a good journey wherever you were off to—sorry we couldn't leap across those dividing glass doors and have a hug! My fellow travellers gave me a wide berth for the rest of my trip home—clearly deciding I was a mad woman, jumping up and down and yelling like that. Thank goodness you turned round when you did—I was running out of party tricks to catch your attention!

And how extraordinary that it should have been Montpellier airport—always one of my favourites—even before they did that gorgeous trick with the sunlight coming through the glass. Do you remember the Spanish tour? That time we got hopelessly lost trying to get out of France and across to Andorra? When was that exactly?

When are you going to come and stay? It's been too long, my dear. My Charly says can you come for her birthday? We're planning a big party. Let me know. You know you're welcome here for as long as you want.

Love to you—as always H.

PS: We loved the show at the National—Bex was outstanding as the mother, so sensitive and powerful; and thanks for the note about the new piece at the Riverside. We'll be there if we can.

Charlie: email

Inner acting

Hey gorgeous, you recognised me, God damn it. I was doing inner acting (it's like the inner smile, only more serious); if you really are the part, I mean, dear heart, *are*, in the *fullest* sense, you don't need makeup. Or funny walks. So I was *being* Donald O'Connor, you know, the immortal Cosmo, in *Singin' in the Rain,* at that precise moment when he jumps off a chair, high in the air, impossibly high, and on his face the essence of joy. And—did you hear?—the guy just died. He had a great life, but everything after that moment must have been ever so slightly downhill. This was my *hommage.* Where was I? Yes, in a chair, in an airport, deadpan face, and inside I was a supreme theatrical moment, absolute concentration, when I was dragged out of vaudeville satori by an unruly rainbow, jumping up and down and waving its arms about. It was you. Toi. And, my darling, I was truly delighted to see you. You had to rush, unfortunately, so you missed my Cosmo walks up the wall imitation, which was strictly an expression of joy at seeing you. It was almost successful, and I didn't break anything (I'm very relaxed nowadays, it's the tai chi: my abdomen is now a lethal weapon, and has to be declared in airports).

OK I'll stop rabbiting on (did Charly get the rabbit suit? Tell her she's my darling). (Yes, of course, the birthday. It's free. Tell her I'll get my people to call her people. That would be wonderful.)

I miss you still. I miss you still.

xx

PS Loved your exhibition, all those rainbows: are you going to tour it anywhere?

Hattie: email

Singin' in the rain

Vaudeville satori! Only you—only you dear Charlie—could come up with a phrase like that… I can feel a song coming on… no time just now… busy busy things to do… but I'd like to pay homage to that marvellous man too… I'll play with it at the weekend and see what comes. Do you remember the night I moved in to that ridiculous, fabulous house in Edgbaston? We did that *Singin' in the Rain* routine then? All my stuff piled up in your hallway—all that rain—so much laughter. I wasn't thinking about it much at the time—but if I had been, I'd have thought I'd died and gone to heaven. God, the relief of meeting up with you two guys! Did Joel dance too? I can't imagine it, but then I can't believe he wouldn't have joined in. We wouldn't have allowed him not to.

Charly is indeed your darling—the rabbit suit is outrageous and completely perfect. Thank you—for that as for so much else.

Glad you liked *Unruly Rainbows!* I'm looking at other venues for it—but the space has to be right—that huge whiteness at Gerda's barn—and that wash of filtered sunlight suits them so well. It's hard to find a space with that much clarity. I'll keep looking, though. Any ideas?

When you come and stay (yes that IS a hint) you can see the new project. I know you'll love it!

When when when will you be here?—we want you here with us!!!!

Love as always H.

Charlie: email

The past is present

Yes, I remember, I remember. Some part of me is still there, singing in the rain. Joel danced, shyly, laughing. It was a long time ago, it was yesterday, it is now.

I feel quite strange, now, writing that. The past is present, weighing, questioning.

I'll go and practice walking up the wall. As I explained to the security police at the airport, you have to keep practising. They were quite good about it, actually, particularly after I told them who I was. That was because I told them I was Sir John Gielgud. They doubted me at first, but my impromptu 'rogue and peasant slave' speech persuaded them. Passersby threw money. People are so kind.

Something is happening, moving, isn't it? Can you feel it?

Love. Always.

xxC

Hattie: email

The right time

Ah—you've noticed it too—I wondered when we would speak it. Or when it would get spoken. Or when it would, itself, speak. I'm serious about you coming to stay, love. I know how tight your schedules are—but this is important. As important as ever. There's something very fine and light and golden emerging along with the return of the sadness. This particular entry into Autumn—it's the right time. The truth is that I've discovered something rather amazing and strange whilst sorting out the piles of books in the study. It's something that Joel wrote years ago—it looks like a bit of a filmscript. I won't say more about it now. I want to see your reaction when you read it yourself. I came across it just the day before our sweet meeting in Montpellier. There are shivers running down my spine just thinking about what this might mean.

I'll attach my diary commitments for the next three weeks—just come when you can—and just turn up unannounced if you want to—you know where everything is.

I was on the phone an hour ago with a friend who's a Benedictine Nun in an abbey near here—she says today is The Feast of Angels. I checked that out with Joel. He smiled and said 'every day is the Feast of Angels,' and then—wait for it—he smiled that amazing smile that I've only ever seen on him—no-one else—ever—that sweet combination of extremely wise and extremely innocent—maybe that's the secret of wisdom? or indeed the secret of true innocence?—anyway he smiled the smile that says 'you're really going to like this…' and said—'if you believe in days.' He sends love, of course. As I do. You know that.

Always, H

PS: Charly can't wait to see the walking up walls routine—wants you to show her how it's done. DON'T YOU DARE!

Charlie: email

I will be there

Joel. Ah. And angels. Yes.

I will come, of course. There's a big meeting of Clowns Incorporated I have to go to, we're getting near to lift-off (lift-off=one clown for every children's ward in the country—minimum) and we're doing a get-together to celebrate and energise and (dis)organise it. Formal dress required: everyone comes suited up, facepaint and all. Amazing what it does to a committee meeting, discussing heavy finance with an accountant, when everyone has these ludicrous smiles painted on their faces. After that, I have some personal space before rehearsals start for the next extravaganza, and I will be there.

The walking up walls is not exactly perfected yet. More an aspiration, really. I have the bruises to prove it. I am however developing a combo clown and rabbit act, a vaudeville number, the two Charlies, kind of a ventriloquism thing except the dummy won't behave, and turns out to have special rabbit superpowers. There's a very good martial arts sequence. Tell dear C to go into training now.

And I will be there. In the golden autumn. With love and expectation of whatever may be.

xxC

Hattie: email

She who cries out

Thank you. Thank you. Charly's so excited—and has all sorts of (rather classy) ideas about the rabbit superpowers. And me—I am just so happy that we'll have some time together Precious precious time.

Now here's something interesting I came across today...

> I am she.
> I am a woman's voice calling, calling;
> And I am cast forth now to meet the face of the world.
> I knead the dough and shape my mind quietly within.
> I am the knowledge of my name.
>
> Listen to my call, you who can hear me,
> And receive my words, you who know me.
> I am the hearing that waits in everything
> At every moment;
> I am the speech that cannot be spoken.

I am the name; the sound
And the sound; the name.
I am.

Who do you think is speaking? Answers on a pc (or mac) please.

Love love love and more

H

Charlie: email

Exit, nightfall

My God, where do you get this stuff? Did you write it? It's astonishing. I can't place it at all. I see a dark stage and a woman in an intense spotlight, straight to audience, but I can't see what to put round it to make a play of it, because it resists category and interpretation so fundamentally. Subversive, it is. And, in the middle of that, the so womanly breadmaking mindmaking image. I am astonished.

It reminds me for some reason of *Animula vagula blandula*. You know? Emperor Hadrian's death poem?

> Soul, my friend, ready to go
> nervously, to what bleak place
> where there are no more jokes.

Everyone has translated it, mostly badly. Prior got the first two lines rather well

> Poor, little, pretty, fluttering thing,
> Must we no longer live together?

but the rest is crap. However, Whitman did a fantastic translation of it. Mind you, he was dying too, when he did it:

> Good-bye, my Fancy! Farewell, dear mate, dear love!
> I'm going away, I know not where,
> Or to what fortune, or whether I may ever see you again,
> So good-bye, my Fancy. Now for my last—let me look
>   back a moment;
> The slower fainter ticking of the clock is in me,
> Exit, nightfall, and soon the heart-thud stopping.

I don't think the Emperor Hadrian knew a lot about death, though, do you? Mind you, I expect he never played the Glasgow Empire, boom boom! Or a schools matinee in Birmingham Rep. I, my dear, have done both. In the latter I was Malvolio, and the audience hated us. They really loathed us. Coldly. Olivia was in tears at the interval, dearest Ali, so I nipped in front of the curtain in full costume and gave them the title song from *Jailhouse Rock,* with the dance sequence, the whole works. The audience became sentient with some alacrity, I can tell you, so I did it again, and, possibly inadvisably, put a little, er, camp into it. So not only did the whole cohort of Birmingham schoolkids that year get the wrong idea about *Twelfth Night,* they also got *entirely* the wrong idea about Elvis Presley. Letters were written. I was sacked. Tickets were sold. I was rehired. It was great.

Anyway, precious, listen, I'm coming to Henley tonight. This (what? I don't know) is important. I called the clowns and told them something urgent has come up. They twitched a little, but it's time they learned the joined up writing, high time; and they know much more than they think they do. So my wonderful PA is even now on her way with rather a lot of very nice bottles of Gigondas and a few other goodies and props and things, luckily she has an HGV licence. I'll pick up a car and come direct from Gatwick. Don't think of meeting me, I'll be there before you know it, how wonderful!

xxC

Hattie: email

Drunk with love

Darling—how wonderful indeed—everything feels lighter and IS brighter just knowing you're on your way (cue for song: on your way/back home).

I'll tell you all about the astonishing quotation when I see you (TONIGHT!!! I can't quite take it in!) —and although you probably won't get this before you arrive (or does that funny little hand-held gadget thing receive email?) I want to get this poem from Joel down on the page straight away. At least I think it's a poem—we loved your translation of the death poem—you've managed to make it so trim and sound so personal to you without sentimentalising at all—I knew the Whitman of course—and isn't there a Pope or a Byron somewhere?—you capture it just so—as you always do.

Our Gigondas awaits you—longing to be drunk—as I am already—drunk with love for you—for us—for us all.

Joel sends love and says this: if you had a soul, and if it could speak, it would tell you this:

> not little at all
> and not only
> but also
> beyond those ideas you have of
> my body
> my guest
> my companion.
> my friend
> my soul
> who are you?
> I ask again and
> again
> who are you?
>
> leave your ideas
> with your hat and your coat
> in the cloakroom
> and be true witness
> to the show
> the passing show
> and there's the joke.
>
> laugh
> you might
> as well
> now
> and here
> right here
> that's the beautiful
> and only
> joke

Charlie: email

Clown nose

Yes gadget gets email. Poem stunning. Will leave hat and coat in cloak-room, keep clown nose though. Soon, love xxc

PS When did Joel get to like Berthold Brecht? Or is that hat and coat in cloakroom reference a coincidence? Ah! No! I've just remembered—a late night argument about *Arturo Ui*. Just after Finals. OK. Delete query. Like poem even more now.

Hattie: email

That extraordinary time

Hello dear Charlie—in haste—loads of people to see today—but just wanting to say how wonderful it was to spend that extraordinary time with you on Sunday/Monday. I know you know that—but it's good to express it too.

Thanks so much for your sweet attentions to Charly—she was in heaven—and still is! I'm not sure the rabbit suit will ever come off! She'd better not grow too quickly!

I'm so happy you saw the water garden—I'm thinking of working down there—in the summer at least—what do you think?

And as for the BIG IDEA—I am over the moon and somewhere out towards Neptune—and probably about to spin off into a neighbouring galaxy or two. It feels so right doesn't it? How lovely that we stayed up all night talking about it—just like it used to be. Remember that *Tempest* thing? That was an all-nighter as I recall. Glad the Gigondas supported us in good health through the yawning dawn and thereafter.

Anyway—must go—more later or soon—love as always Hattie.

PS—I thought I might send that Jung lecturer a 'thank you—you were wonderful and made all the difference' card—or email—or something. I can't for the life of me remember her name—a Freudian slip? I'm sure you do—people-person incorporated—do you think she's still in Bir-mingham? Perhaps you could check her out for me on some worldly web thing? Thanks. xxH

Charlie: email

Speechless

Just snatching some space from circumstance to say, what can I say? Speechless, me, really? Yes. Yes. Thank you, I guess. Thank you for your fire. You know something? All that wine (that beautiful wine) and no hangover: I was crystal clear working with (playing with) the gorgeous child next day. In an altered state, sure, but kind of exalted, too, tasting purity.

Your hair in the firelight; your animation. The silences, laughter, peace.

Oh, and the water garden. A little valley of peace, and the sound of water: how well tuned your waterfall is. To sit in there is like being held in the cup of God's hand. Next time, there will be time, and I will sit seriously.

Oh, and the big idea. The really really big idea. What's the first step? I'd like to write something. I'd like to write the scene where little Hattie is taught by her Dad the story of *Can't Catch Me*. Would that be OK? Do you mind me doing that bit? I can so much visualise it and hear it. Little H might be a little undissimilar to little C, but that's not a problem, is it?

And Joel is going to write more of this with us?

Back to the circumstance. On with the motley. Literally: clowns' followup meeting, which traditionally starts with solo acts, showing where we each are now with the medium. Christ that sounds serious. I am turning into an academic. No, no, *anything* but that, which reminds me, how could you have forgotten her name: Ariel Andrews. The child of Shakespeare scholars. Lovely, isn't it, as of course was she. a.k.andrews@bham.ac.uk. That's where it all began, cue for wobbly fade and wobbly music and flashback. Is that where it began? What indeed is a beginning? Oh God there he is, the inner academic again. I see him as a slime mould, in an early horror film, you know, the ones with the rather brilliant crap colour values?

INT. LECTURE ROOM. MORNING.

Cut to: face of CHARLIE, *close-up, looking horrified: pan away, he's looking at his hand, which is covered with green goo; close-up of goo: scary chords: it's spreading! Cut back to face, oh my God, green goo too.*

CHARLIE

All closures are illusory, true, but has no-one considered the concept, opener?

Where was I? I don't know. Motley, motley, I must away.

Love. Love like a fire in the night.

xxC

PS Can you send me a copy of the piece you read me? Amazing that it should have come to light after all these years. Did Joel show it to you at the time?

Hattie: email

Dad

Oh I would love you to write the *Can't Catch Me* piece. Dad would adore that too. I'm going to see him in a day or two. I'll tell him all about it. He'll be pleased. For us. And maybe, deep inside himself somewhere, flattered that you want to write up his story. He's as extraordinary as ever. Quieter since Mum died. But so relieved that she didn't survive the stroke and linger in distress. Not a selfish cell in his dear body or his generous mind.

Me, I'd like to do that very first meeting—that lecture. Is that OK with you? Well—I'll just go ahead—and we can always re-write or re-shape each other's scenes, can't we? I am so excited I can't settle to anything today.

How could I have forgotten a name like Ariel Andrews? We'll have to call her something else though won't we? No-one will believe that name.

And Joel? Well of course he'll be writing with us. Dear Joel. How he would have loved that happy, magical long night by the autumn fireside. Charlie—you do know how much you mean to me don't you?

Little Charly has painted a picture of you. She clearly hasn't spotted the inner academic. It's quite a good likeness in its way—very colourful—very splashy. Huge smile and widespread arms and hands.

All ready to hug her—she says. She's clearly in love.

Me too.

H

PS Joel says that he wants to tinker with that piece of his that I showed you the other night, so I'll leave it with him, and send it on to you when he's done that. I might have to sneak it off him at some point—always a perfectionist, our dear man. No, he never showed it to me at the time.

He's a bit surprised it was still tucked away with his book collection. He thought he'd burned it. Though he might have been joking when he said that. Guess which book I found it in, by the way.

Hattie: email

Begun

Well—I've begun! Not sure how wordy to make it—nor how much like a regular film script. Any suggestions? I guess the thing to do is to just write at this stage—and do all of that shaping and tidying later. It's been ages since I wrote dialogue… I'm having to stop myself hearing hooks for good songs! Maybe I'll keep them separately somewhere in my ever-growing file of 'good ideas for songs'.

I feel very happy, very contented. This is absolutely the right thing to be doing right now.

Here's a wonderful Rumi poem for you—I tinkered with it a bit…

> Today, look: another day; waking, wide open,
> Afraid. Don't dive into the library,
> Into yet another book. Reach for your guitar,
> Let love, let beauty, be what it is we do:
> You don't have to fly abroad, in order to kneel
> And kiss the tarmac!

So—much love to you.

Hattie: email

Worried

Hey sweetheart—are you OK? I've left a couple of messages on your answerphone… No need to reply if you're just busy—but I'm worried not to have heard from you for a few days.

Love to you.

H

Charlie: email

Unexpected

I hadn't anticipated what this would bring up. Sorry, dearest, sorry. It was completely unexpected. Will write tonight. xxC

Charlie: email

Shocked

Hello my heart:

OK have given self a good talking to and pulled said self together. I am shocked at how much it got to me, to go back there, go back then. I found there were rather a lot of tears to shed, still; for that young man Charlie, for Joel, for you, for me and you. Then I flung myself headlong into all the things I am involved with at the moment, emails, phone calls, doing voices, make them laugh, the great thing about the contracted world is that there's always someone for whom it is daytime, who can therefore be phoned and talked to, at any time of the night. I haven't slept much.

Yes, I'm fine. Really fine. A clown in tears? Such *schmaltz,* darling. I am fine.

Look, I've done a scene. I think it's a pre-credit sequence. It's when your Dad came down unexpectedly because he decided you had gone off the rails—remember? Because you had told him about the Provençal project?

We are going to put the Provençal stuff into the movie, are we? We are going to risk and expose all that, that secret story, the heart's blood?

I was in the Pyrenees recently, driving through. A sign said: welcome to Cathar country.

Well, yes. Welcome, all of us, back to Cathar country.

xxC

Hattie: email

Bigger

Yes—I know what you mean—I'm just so relieved to know you're OK—I guess that's part of it. Strange isn't it—we coped so amazingly well at the time... That wasn't just youthfulness was it? It seemed like wisdom then.

Let's please stay in touch now—no more long silences—no more short silences. Not like me to be that nervous or this demanding I know—but this is bigger than I realised it would be.

I'm going down to the water garden now to read your scene. There's too much bustle here to concentrate properly. I have to confess I'm so excited about it. So I'm probably indulging myself in delayed gratification too. Dad was right. The middle class ethos got to me eventually! Poor Dad!

Love to you.

Hattie

Charlie: filmscript 1

Meet my friends

INT. CHARLIE'S HOUSE: KITCHEN—AFTERNOON

APRIL 1972

HATTIE is on the phone

HATTIE

Yes, I'm fine, of course; did you get my letter? Don't you think it's a great idea? ... Yes, of course I'm OK, what are you worried about? (PAUSE. LAUGHS). Yes of course I've smoked dope. No, it's not a regular thing, just every now and then. ... Dad, you really don't have to worry. Look, this is really important to me. I'm sharing it with you. ... Yes, it's set in the twelfth century. ... No, it's bigger than that, it's bigger than that: look, trust me, OK?

INT. CHARLIE'S HOUSE. MUSIC ROOM—MORNING

HATTIE SITTING AT THE PIANO, PYJAMAS, LOADS OF PIECES OF PAPER AROUND, WRITING A SONG. EARLY SUNDAY MORNING. TRYING THINGS ON PIANO, WRITING THEM DOWN.

DOORBELL. HATTIE STICKS A PENCIL BEHIND EAR AND MAKES TO MOVE.

INT. CHARLIE'S HOUSE: HALLWAY—MOMENTS LATER

HATTIE OPENS DOOR. HER FATHER IS STANDING THERE IN SUIT AND TIE. THEY LOOK AT EACH OTHER. SHE'S SURPRISED; HE LOOKS WORRIED AND DISAPPROVING.

HATTIE
Dad, what are you doing here?

FATHER
I'm worried about you, I couldn't sleep, I got the early train.

INT. CHARLIE'S HOUSE: KITCHEN—MOMENTS LATER

FATHER IS LOOKING AROUND: HE HASN'T BEEN THERE BEFORE. LOOKS EVEN
MORE WORRIED: 'WHERE HAVE I COME TO?' HATTIE IS SITTING OPPOSITE:
A POT OF TEA ON THE KITCHEN TABLE, MUGS IN FRONT OF EACH.

HATTIE
What do you think of the place, then?

FATHER
Money. It reeks of money. How much rent do you pay?

HATTIE
I don't.

FATHER
You pay nothing, for this? (LOOKS EVEN MORE WORRIED).

HATTIE
(A 'WHERE DO I BEGIN?' LOOK)

Dad, it's not like that.

FATHER LOOKS DISAPPROVING, ALIENATED, UNCOMFORTABLE IN HIS SUIT
AND TIE.

HATTIE (CONT'D)
You can relax, you know, this is my home you're in.

FATHER UNCERTAIN.

JOEL (O.S.)
(SINGING)

JOEL BACKS IN, WEARING A FLORAL PINAFORE, SCARF TIED ROUND HEAD
MRS. MOP FASHION, RUBBER GLOVES, FEATHER DUSTER, BUCKET IN OTHER
HAND; HE IS DEDICATEDLY CLEANING, ALSO SINGING, RATHER CAMP. HE IS
DOING HIS MRS. MOP ACT, WHICH HE DOES REGULARLY; HE WANTS TO GET
THE PLACE CLEAN, AND HIS STANDARD OF CLEANNESS IS HIGHER THAN THE
OTHERS, SO IN ORDER NOT TO BE A CLEANNESS FASCIST (OR HIS MOTHER)
HE SENDS IT UP, AND THEREFORE EVERYONE HAS A NICE TIME.

JOEL SEES HATTIE'S MESS OF PAPERS, DOES A FALSETTO SCREAM:

JOEL (CONT'D)
Mess, mess, everywhere mess!

HATTIE
Joel, touch those papers and die.

JOEL
I give my life to this house. And what happens? Mess. Nothing but mess.

HATTIE
Joel, I'd like you to meet my father.

JOEL
Ah. Mr. Tattersall. (ORDINARY VOICE).

JOEL STICKS OUT HAND (WITH RUBBER GLOVE ON IT). THEY BOTH LOOK AT THE HAND WITH RUBBER GLOVE. NOISE OF HORN OFF. PARP PARP. THEY LOOK AT EACH OTHER. FATHER'S FACE: 'WHAT THE HELL IS THAT?' JOEL'S FACE: 'OH NO, THIS IS NOT HAPPENING'. HATTIE'S FACE: STARTING TO SMILE.

ENTER CHARLIE, REHEARSING: FULL CLOWN OUTFIT, BIG BOOTS, HORN. PERCEIVES AN AUDIENCE, AHA! AND AUTOMATICALLY GOES INTO AN IMPROV.

CHARLIE
Ladies and gentleman, so glad you stopped by.

FALLS FLAT ON BOTTOM, PARP. SPRINGS TO FEET.

CHARLIE (CONT'D)
(TO JOEL) Madam, please introduce me to your friend (THE DUSTER): she reminds me of someone I knew. God, she was beautiful. (STAGE ASIDE) A bit of a featherbrain, actually. (TO DUSTER): a real bird of paradise (SE-DUCES THE DUSTER).

HATTIE
Charlie, I'd like you to meet my father.

CHARLIE
Ah. Mr. Tattersall. (PUTS OUT HAND. A BUNCH OF FLOWERS SHOOTS OUT OF HIS SLEEVE.) Ah. Sorry. Er.

THE MEN STAND IN A TABLEAU OF HOPELESS IMPASSE AND DISCOMFORT. HATTIE BEGINS TO LAUGH AND LAUGH (HER AMAZING LAUGH).

HATTIE

OK, you men, stop looking at each other like this, I can't bear it. Dad, come with me, we're going down the pub.

SHE TAKES A BIG OVERCOAT AND SCARF FROM KITCHEN DOOR. PUTS IT ON OVER PYJAMAS.

HATTIE (CONT'D)

Charlie, go to the off-licence and get some beer. Joel, food, please. We'll see you for lunch. We'll be back at one o'clock.

INT. PUB—LATER

BIG BIRMINGHAM PUB, RAMBLING, FRIENDLY, WORKING CLASS. A PINT OF BEER EACH.

HATTIE AND HER FATHER ARE TALKING VERY INTENSELY, A BIG ARGUMENT, HEAD TO HEAD, VERY DISPUTATIOUS, BUT LOVING ALSO. TIME PASSES. HATTIE IS INTENSE AND NOT LAUGHING; SO ENERGISED YOU COULD AL-MOST THINK SHE WAS ANGRY. IN FACT SHE'S STANDING UP FOR HERSELF. QUITE A LOT OF BEER IS DRUNK. FATHER TOO GETS ANIMATED, LOSES THE APPEARANCE OF MEEKNESS THAT HE HAD IN THE HOUSE.

HATTIE

Of course I still care about the class struggle, of course I do. But this is my vision. This is my work. This is me. I won't be tied by your expecta-tions of me. I owe you almost everything; now let me go.

FATHER

(SHOCKED. INTERNAL STRUGGLE) You are turning your back on every-thing that is important.

HATTIE

No, I'm turning my face towards what is important to me.

FATHER

Religion is a drug to keep the oppressed in a state of pig ignorance.

HATTIE

My programme is not about religion, it's about the life of the spirit.

FATHER

There's no difference, it's all lies.

HATTIE

I'll show you the difference. Come and meet my friends.

FATHER

The clown and the fool.

HATTIE

When did you become a man who put people in categories?

FATHER

(STARES INTO HIS BEER) Since I became frightened something would harm my precious daughter.

HATTIE IS CAUGHT, AND SOFTENS. TOUCHES ARM. LOVING LOOKS INTER-CHANGED, HE SLIGHTLY EMBARRASSED.

HATTIE

Come on, Comrade Dad, come and meet my friends.

INT. CONCERT HALL: SMALL—EVENING

WHILE THE CREDITS RUN, WE SEE CHARLIE, NO LONGER IN CLOWN OUT-FIT, JOEL, NO LONGER MRS MOP, AND HATTIE, NO LONGER IN PYJAMAS, PERFORMING A SONG [ONE OF THE EARLY ONES—WHICH ONE WOULD YOU LIKE?]. HATTIE IS AT THE PIANO; JOEL IS LEAD GUITAR AND CHARLIE BASS. JOEL IS WEARING A YARMULKE.

Hattie: email

Cheered

Charlie—I love the scene! My God—that day is as crystal clear in my memory as yesterday! I'm feeling remarkably cheered by it—that routine with the duster was so brilliant. Do you remember poor Dad's face? He was so shocked by you two I'm sure he didn't even notice that I was go-ing out in my pyjamas! You've captured the essential details of my time in the pub with Dad just about perfectly. I'm enclosing what I was think-ing of as the opening—but I like yours much better. Maybe these chunks could come just afterwards? They are about when we met, and the Jung lecture, and Ariel Andrews. I've copied your layout a bit, because I don't know anything about how to set out film scripts, but I couldn't bear all those capitals; we can get someone to tidy it up later.

Do you think a trip to Birmingham would be a good idea? I haven't been there in years—and I try not to read the squirm-making alumni mag when it shows up! The house must still be there mustn't it? And we could surprise Ariel Andrews. Maybe that's a silly idea.

I do think we should take a trip to France together though—don't you? Those brown signs are ghastly aren't they? Cathars for tourists—there's a deeply ironic prose piece lurking in there somewhere—what greater absurdity? I wonder if there are Cathar trinkets on sale in those places—and if so, what on earth would they dream up? We could set up a competition for the most ludicrously inappropriate Cathar souvenir!

Yes dear—all that secret material definitely. Joel says it couldn't have been said before this—and he should know, if anyone does. I hope we can say it in the right way. Joel's laughing at me. Not a great supporter of self-doubt is Joel—at least not these days. Me, I seem to have fallen into it big time—strange to be reconnecting with the young woman who was so certain and so secure in what she thought she knew. No—actually—in what she knew she knew.

How good life is. Go well.

PS I think any of the early songs would do nicely there—what would you choose?

Hattie: filmscript 2

The lecture

INT: THE UNIVERSITY: A LECTURE THEATRE—MORNING

It's a cold clear October morning, in 1970. Camera pans around full auditorium in large lecture theatre. 1970 music is playing on soundtrack.

(Must think of some music to put in here, can you remember what we used to listen to then?)

A lecture is happening; we can't hear the words. Camera lingers on HAT-TIE, CHARLIE, and JOEL in the audience. CHARLIE and JOEL are sitting together. The lecturer is female and dazzlingly gorgeous, a mellifluous voice. A beautiful mover. Liquid gestures: a joy to watch. Autumn sunlight through windows.

It's that time of year when clothing is still light, but people are beginning to put jumpers on. The students are dressed in early 70's clothing, colourful and eclectic. HATTIE is dressed in clashing oranges and pinks; she has long curly ginger hair. She is clearly unconventional and happy to stand out in the crowd. JOEL *wears jeans and a plain sweater, a little crocheted yarmulke. You know he doesn't think clothes are important. Apart from his yarmulke and his striking and strong face, he is invisible.* CHARLIE *is elegant and interesting; he dresses all in black, his clothes understated and expensive. He has the body and physical ease of a dancer.*

Focus on female lecturer. Sound fades up.

ARIEL ANDREWS

And, if we switch this insight across to the literary, then we can say that in that moment of apprehension, known to us all, that beautiful creative moment when the poem comes into existence in the reader's mind, that perfect moment of understanding and creation, like a new morning: we can say that this too is, finally, a lesson in love.

Stunned silence: applause. The actors represent the following internal voices with facial expressions only:

HATTIE

(Internal voice) Wow, at last, that's what I call a lecture. Hattie, you're back on track.

JOEL

(Internal voice) Thank God. Now there's a way of making sense of it all. It was right to come back, after all. Thank God.

CHARLIE

(Internal voice) That was sensational; just sensational. If I could capture just a bit of that and put it on stage, there'd be no stopping me.

ARIEL ANDREWS

OK, Part 2 next week. Do the preliminary reading won't you? And … thanks for your attention.

She sweeps out of a door at the back of the room. Students start gathering books together, preparing to go.

There is a general hubbub, people bunch up going out of the door and HATTIE, JOEL, *and* CHARLIE *end up next to each other.* JOEL *drops a book;* HATTIE *and* CHARLIE *stoop to pick it up and both hold it for a clumsy moment. It's a battered copy of Jung's* Memories, Dreams, Reflections. *They look at each other briefly and go off in separate directions.*

Soundtrack still has 1970's music playing.

Charlie: email

Purity

She was amazing, the young Hattie. I had never seen anyone with such purity, toughness, simplicity, she was as clear, and as hard, as telling the truth. And those eyes, that did not let go, did not back off. When we found out that she could play the piano just like ringing a bell, well, it was love, it was love.

Your scene is great. That chunk of lecture just captures the excitement of it; ah, I remember. But I don't think going back is a good idea, I think maybe the place would look sad, and scruffy, diminished, in the pale light of day. You forget, my love: we have been around. We have done things, and do. We tend to shine. I can see it: that dingy corridor, no windows, cowed students; academics blinking bemusedly, in the sunlight of your hair. And, you know, I do have this lamentable tendency, when faced with constriction, to, er, liven things up?

But France, yes, that is different. It would be unbearable, to go back there, to go where it hurts. We must do it. But not yet; what we must do now is to imagine back to that golden time of meeting and finding out.

You go on with the narrative of meeting, my love: *Jules et Jim,* and the rest of that beautiful evening. It's your (her) POV, meeting these two men, their house, their friendship.

I'm entranced with creating the young—younger—Hattie, and her father. And thinking too about the twelfth century Provençal material. Thinking very hard about how to do the quality of it, the colours and brightness—what was it that Oxford Prof of yours said, the springtime of the world? A dream, as real as a dream, sharp and bright and true and longed for, perfect, visionary.

Goodnight, beloved.

xxC

PS Why not invite Ariel to visit? Send a car for her? Ask Murray if he'd like to do it, they would have a lot to say to each other. You could get him a chauffeur's outfit, white, I think (call my PA with his measurements) and a ridiculously huge bunch of very red roses.

Hattie: email

Practical plan

Thanks for your message—marvellous as always. No time for a proper response right now—a million and one things to do. Am working on the next scenes—and will get them to you as soon as I can. Do we need to do things in order? We probably need to meet up quite soon to make a practical plan (rather than—or as well as—the visionary one!) Charly is going to Zurich for half term in the week beginning October 27th so, with Murray and Kes here to take care of the animals, I'll be free to come to one of your places if that would fit with your plans better? You know you're welcome here if you prefer.

Love to you—sorry to be in such a rush

Hattie

PS Murray loves the white suit/limo/red roses plan. It made me laugh out loud to think of that gorgeous, outstanding, big, powerful man doing his gentle elephant-footed walk down that long corridor. It would be wonderful in slo-mo… But that's another movie maybe.

C has just come in from a party (another party!)… And sends high pitched squeals of love in your direction. Same from me—but with more decorum (sadly!)

PPS (or is this PPPS?) I don't think of the corridor as dingy and windowless at all—don't you remember the squeaky clean red lino floor (and the funny noise of K.J.White's desert boots as he strode forward to do intellectual battle?) And that little bay in the middle of the corridor that let light in—and the luscious cherry tree blossom in May? We all used to congregate there before such classes as we deigned to turn up for! Oh—the dreadful coffee from the Mason Lounge downstairs—just remembered how awful the taste was—I am going to go and make a wonderful espresso and sit at my desk and write today's song!

Hattie: email

Is it too wordy?

Hello dear—here it is—what do you think? Is it too wordy? HELP please. I'm a songwriter not a screenplaywriter.

love

Hattie

Hattie: filmscript 3

Jules et Jim

INT. SMALL CINEMA IN ARTS CENTRE—EVENING

A couple of days after the lecture. We see the closing credits of Jules et Jim *and hear the closing music.* HATTIE, JOEL, *and* CHARLIE *are sitting in the auditorium in the same configuration as in the lecture hall.* JOEL *and* CHARLIE *next to each other,* HATTIE *by herself a few rows away. Everyone else is pushing past them to leave the cinema, whilst they are sitting there determined to see all the credits and eventually are the only ones left in the cinema. They coalesce at the door, come out into the light, and see each other clearly.*

HATTIE

Hey, you two again! I don't know if you noticed but we were all in that amazing Jung lecture yesterday.

JOEL

The Jung lecture—hey!

HATTIE

Could be something in this synchronicity business, perhaps?

CHARLIE

We'd better find out, hadn't we? Come and have a drink.

INT. ARTS CENTRE BAR

Hubbub of people, arty atmosphere, paintings on walls.

Background music (jazz, I think, don't you?)

The three are sitting together at a small table. HATTIE *has pastis,* CHARLIE *has a pint of beer,* JOEL *has a fruit juice.*

CHARLIE

OK, you start: who are you?

HATTIE

Hattie Tattersall, 4th year English and French, just back from a year in Toulouse, which, believe me, is a place worth knowing. Until that lecture yesterday I wished I hadn't come back. Now all I want to do is to find out where to go next, how to get that stuff into my life.

JOEL

Right, exactly. Joel Cohen. Third year straight English. Until last year I knew exactly where I was going. I'm still down for rabbinical college and I used to be a passionate Zionist. I spent the summer in Israel, and something happened, and the whole thing fell apart. But since that lecture yesterday I think there might be a way forward.

HATTIE

What happened?

JOEL

It's hard to talk about.

Long pause: looks at HATTIE, *thinks about it; looks to* CHARLIE, *who has already heard it;* CHARLIE *nods reassuringly. Close focus on* JOEL'S *face during the telling of this story; we need to engage with the pain of it and the beauty of this man.*

JOEL

I was travelling in the desert, sitting with a group of friends in the back of an open truck, and we went past the aftermath of a bombing.

FLASHBACK

JOEL (VOICE-OVER)

Feelings were high; for me too. I saw a dead body, huddled on the ground, its face blown away, a broken body. You couldn't tell whether it was a Jew or an Arab. You just couldn't tell. All I knew at that moment was that somewhere a family would be grieving, and at that point everything I thought I believed in fell apart, because it came to me that it made no difference, no difference at all: Jew or Arab; no difference.

HATTIE

A human life is a human life.

JOEL

Yes. Exactly. However beautiful and profound the belief system that brought me up, if in any way it contradicts that, or can be used to contradict that, then I can't be part of it. That's it: that's what it comes down to. That's enough. Your turn, Charlie.

CHARLIE

(A loving smile at JOEL; they are not in competition here.)

OK, how to follow that? Charlie Beaumont, English and Drama, third year. My thing is this. I'm an actor, a director: that's what I do. And I'm good at it. I've always known that. Well, this is nothing compared with Joel's experience, but it's important to me. This summer I was supposed to put on a production of *Pericles* in Edinburgh. Right: a difficult play. No idea how to stage it. Then, I know this sounds mad, but I had a dream; in the dream I was dreaming, and the dream was *Pericles*. I woke up and saw that the play was a dream, a dream within a dream.

HATTIE

What do you mean?

CHARLIE

Do you know *Pericles?*

HATTIE

I read it, a while ago.

CHARLIE

OK, imagine it this way: here is a man dreaming his life, from young manhood to old age. At the end, he wakes up, and finds he is still dreaming.

HATTIE

Wow, did you know about Jung?

CHARLIE

Not till yesterday, that's the amazing thing.

JOEL

(Breaking in)

You have to know that the production was a huge success. Wonderful reviews in all of the classy papers, TV coverage, the lot: this man is a star, and everyone wants to know why he came back to this place to finish reading English.

CHARLIE

Well, I was wondering too.

HATTIE

It's obvious: so that we could hear that lecture, and so that we three could meet.

JOEL

Oh no: this is the curse of *Jules et Jim.* I can't bear it when life imitates art.

HATTIE

(Laughs her well-known stop-them-in-their-tracks laugh)

You'd better get used to it. Let's go back in and watch it again, so that we can find out what we're supposed to do.

INT. SMALL CINEMA IN ARTS CENTRE

The close of Jules et Jim *again—further on in music and credits. The three of them sitting together,* HATTIE *in the middle. They stay sitting to end of credits.*

JOEL

This is going to be a long conversation. Come back to our place. We've got a spare room, you can sleep there if you want.

EXT. CHARLIE'S HOUSE

They've walked here. They arrive at the gate to the drive of a very big white Georgian house in Edgbaston.

CHARLIE

This is it.

HATTIE

My God, you're joking.

JOEL

Afraid not.

They walk up a gravel drive to a huge house; it's both stylish and rather decrepit. The surroundings are very very elegant, with that layer of scruffi-ness that comes from a big house with no housekeeper.

HATTIE

Where did you find a fantastic place like this? I'm in a bedsit in Selly Oak!

CHARLIE

Sorry about this. My parents are loaded. My father bought it. He'll sell it when I leave and make a big profit.

They arrive at the big front door. CHARLIE *opens it. The hall is already lit and inviting.*

INT. CHARLIE'S HOUSE: KITCHEN.

Big table in kitchen; oil-burning Aga. Pots and pans hanging up; it's messy but absolutely not dirty. Bright colours, blues, yellows. No flowers as yet: HATTIE *will bring flowers. Books everywhere. Sheet music. Posters on the wall.*

JOEL

OK, I'm the Jewish mother; I do the food and drink. What do you want?

HATTIE

(The famous laugh)

If you're going to be a Jewish mother you'd better choose, because we won't get it right.

JOEL

(Laughs)

I'll see to it. I know my place.

He moves away from the other two—sounds of him preparing food in background and out of view.

CHARLIE *puts on a record. It's medieval plainsong—quietly in background.*

HATTIE

(Taking the bull by the horns)

So: how do you feel about having all this money, then?

CHARLIE

I can handle it: it's really useful; you can cut so many corners with money. The problem is, the way other people react to it. So how do *you* feel about my parents being rich?

HATTIE

Well, up to a year ago I'd have thought of you as the enemy. Straight away, no questions asked. My father's a shop steward and he hates the fucking bosses. So tea-time conversation—tea, you know, not dinner—taught me all I thought I needed to know about the way this country really works.

CHARLIE

So what happened a year ago, then?

HATTIE

Wait till Joel comes back—I'd like to tell you both—it's important. Let's just say: I saw the big picture. I don't understand any of it, but I know this, I saw it, and it changed everything. Everything.

CHARLIE

(sings)

That transcendental, it'll drive you mental—if the booze don't get you then the acid will.

HATTIE

(laughs)

Funny you should say that ...

CHARLIE *picks up a cane and a hat that are lying around and does a funny little Chaplinesque dance—very skilfully.*

His dance gets more elaborate; moves into the style of Olivier in the film of The Entertainer—*equally skilful.*

HATTIE

(impressed and delighted—as Charlie hopes she will be)

How did you learn to do that?

CHARLIE

(in Olivier voice and with Olivier gesture)

My dear, I am a man of the theatre.

JOEL *appears with tray of good things—a big tray, loaded with bagels, dish of chopped herring with fresh parsley on top, smoked salmon with slices of lemon, pickled cucumber, beautifully arranged, three Russian-style glasses of lemon tea with fresh lemon floating in them, plates, knives, cloth napkins. NB There is a vase with a single flower in it—a late autumn flower.*

CHARLIE *makes a flourish of trumpets with his voice.*

JOEL

Eat: enjoy!

HATTIE

Wow! The pair of you are a seriously classy act! Where in God's name did you get bagels in Birmingham?

JOEL

My mother's network, mainly based in north London. It's a trade-off—I get the bagels and she gets the gossip about me. And if you really want to know, these bagels were made by my second cousin's wife's brother's mother-in-law, Mrs. Finkel of Harborne High Street. The chopped herring, on the other hand, comes from a kosher delicatessen in our own beloved north London, and was brought here by my cousin Harry as he was passing through on his way to Glasgow to a bar mitzvah.

HATTIE

(Laughs)

To life!

JOEL has been laying things out on the table. They clink their glasses of lemon tea: 'to life!'

JOEL

So, you speak the language: is that from literature, or from life?

HATTIE

Both: I read a lot, but actually it's from life—my friend Deborah at school used to have me to tea all the time.

JOEL

Deborah Greenbaum?

HATTIE

Almost; Deborah Greenstein.

JOEL

Ah, one of the very few English Jews I'm not related to. But give it time, it's an expanding enterprise.

CHARLIE

When you two have finished schmoozing—I was just about to find out something really interesting here, but she wouldn't tell me until you came back. OK Hattie, here he is, now take it from the top.

HATTIE

With or without feeling?

CHARLIE

Be true to the part, darling, just be true to the part.

HATTIE

A year ago, I was in Toulouse.

Voiceover, with shots of HATTIE *in Toulouse. Music on record player turns out to be appropriate: French medieval plainsong. Shots of Toulouse throughout this passage until indicated otherwise.*

HATTIE

So, there I was, getting by, nothing special. Do you know Toulouse? Red brick, and a whole lot of history.

CHARLIE

Red brick like our own dear University?

HATTIE

No, the whole city is made of this beautiful weathered red brick: soft, it is, and rounded.

JOEL

Not at all like, then.

HATTIE

No. And, unlike our own dear University, history weighs heavy on the whole place all the time. You can feel it: really old betrayals, ancient loves, battles, and a lot of death, everywhere.

(We come back to seeing them in the kitchen here.)

JOEL

Do you mean during the war?

HATTIE

Yes, during the war. The war between France and Occitania.

CHARLIE

Where? Where the hell's Occitania?

HATTIE

Nowhere. Nowhere at all. It was obliterated in the thirteenth century. Before that it was the most vital and vibrant culture in Europe. Roughly, it's Provence.

JOEL

How come we've never heard of this?

HATTIE

There's more than one way to do genocide: and there's more than one way to write history.

JOEL

That's not easy for me, you know that, don't you? But I'll think about it. Go on with the story.

HATTIE

So there I am in a little apartment in the top of an old building, one sunlit Sunday morning in March.

Camera moves to the scene she's describing—shabby, tiny one-room apartment—student accommodation in crumbling old French building. It's strewn with colourful things of HATTIE's that hide the inherent greyness of the room; shawls, scarves, cloths, many books, a guitar, etc.

CHARLIE

(over shots of HATTIE moving about her room)

OK, I have to picture this: by yourself?

HATTIE

In a manner of speaking. I've just taken 1000 micrograms of pretty good acid.

Camera follows her description below—it's visually gorgeous—fuzzy in places—crystal clear in others.

HATTIE

It's springtime. In Toulouse. It's the springtime of the world. The smell of mimosa, and the sound of a skylark, a long way up in the air and singing the song of his heart. I'm in the forest, with sunlight gold through the greenery—I can feel the taste of spring flowers on my lips, the taste of the saffron crocuses and the white garlic flowers humming in my head. It's perfect, and a bit more than perfect: it's just beginning to shimmer. The sense of dazzling uncertainty. The sense of all things new.

Then:

New music fades up—it is similar to the music that CHARLIE put on the record player—but definitely distinct—clearer, a bell-like female voice singing. It is a Provençal song.

> can vei la lauzeta mover
> de joi sas alas contral rai

que so'oblida'e.s laissa chazer
per la soussor c'al cor li vai

when I see the skylark move
with joy his wings against the sun
and so forget himself that, falling,
he dies into his own delight . . .

ai tan grans enveya m'en ve
de cui qu'eu veya jauzion,
meravilhas ai car desse
lo cor de dezirer mno.m fon.

then ah, a great desire comes
to be at one with that delight;
so strange it is, that desire does not
take my heart at once away from me

anc non agui de mon poder
ni no fui meus de l'or'en sai
que.m laisser en sos olhs vezer
en un miralh que mout me plai

I have no sense of being me
nor am I ruler of myself
since in her eyes she let me see
my self. This mirror is delight.

miralhs, pus me merie en te,
m'an mort li sospir de preon,
c'aissi.m perdei com perdet se
lo bels narcuisus en la fon

mirror I mirror me in you
and breathe myself away, and die;
losing me as he was lost
Narcissus at the river's edge

HATTIE

I hear someone singing, in Provençal. I don't know the language, but I understand every word. This beautiful language: the actual language of song. She's singing about love, and the skylark; but what the song is really about is: God.

Close-up on HATTIE in the forest.

HATTIE

And I feel myself remembering something I can't quite remember. I am filled with longing for this thing that's just on the tip of my mind—this—this essence—this something I can't find words for. And it's coming from the song.

Distance shot of the LADY

HATTIE

The Lady who's singing is walking towards me, she's coming out of the green gold sunlight, I can feel her coming nearer.

Close up of the LADY—identical face to HATTIE's—is she HATTIE? She is.

HATTIE

And here she is—we are face to face. She stops singing and looks at me. It's a mirror. I'm looking in a magic mirror. She has a long white gown, a gold necklace—really thin fine gold and orange ribbon in her hair. And: she has my face. Her voice is my voice. She is me.

Picture starts to distort and fragment—beautifully—sumptuous colours—not disturbing particularly.

HATTIE

And when I got that—when that came to me—that she was me—then suddenly everything I thought I knew melted away; everything that kept me separate from everything else completely dissolved and vanished. I remembered. There was just her and me, and then there was just ... That. Nothing but That.

Picture goes into brilliant light—with a hint of fire. We come back to the kitchen—focus on HATTIE's face. The record has finished. There is silence.

HATTIE

And that's it. There's nothing else I can say—either you get it or you don't.

Pause. Camera focus on reaction shots of JOEL and CHARLIE—heightened state—a sense of wonder.

JOEL

(Slowly. He reaches out and thoughtfully touches the flower in the vase before he speaks)

I think we get it.

Looking at the flower—not at the others.

CHARLIE

(Quietly—not being the actor here—without his usual flamboyance)

I heard the song. *(Pause).* I heard the song.

Little pause.

HATTIE

(Laughing and upbeat again: takes a bite from a bagel, and gestures with it)

Bagels are bliss as well! Anyway, I spent the rest of the year looking for that song. I learned a bit of the language. I read some books. I read some music.

CHARLIE

You read music?

HATTIE

Yes, I do.

CHARLIE

Come and look at our music room.

HATTIE

Come on—you're kidding: a music room?

INT. MUSIC ROOM

Downstairs room looking out over garden. Dark parquet floor, French windows to garden, baby grand, couple of old sofas, guitars, music, drums, big high ceiling, rather bare apart from that: minimalist, elegant. Tree outside the window; cherry. It's October—when the leaves are colourful and getting more sparse, but have not yet fallen significantly. Charlie lights a gas fire.

HATTIE

Is that piano in tune?

CHARLIE

(Laughs) That piano is so in tune, it can read your mind.

HATTIE goes to the piano and starts to play and sing 'Crazy Wisdom Lady'.

> crazy wisdom lady
> crazy sunshine day

crazy wisdom lady
are you here to stay?

don't know where I'm bound
don't know where I'm going
guess I'll stick around
tell you what I'm knowing

crazy wisdom lady
crazy sunshine day
crazy wisdom lady
are you here to stay?

don't know what this tune is
don't know what my song's for
guess I'll see it through
tell you what I long for

crazy wisdom lady
crazy sunshine day
crazy wisdom lady
are you here to stay?

big old house, crazy paving
windows let the sunshine in
big old house for misbehaving
won't you let the show begin?

big old house, crazy kitchen
food and drink to make you smile
big old house to stage a sit-in
shall we stay here for a while?

big old house, crazy maybe
two guitars and a keyboard dame
big old house for sweet songs baby
things might never be the same

crazy wisdom lady
crazy sunshine day
crazy wisdom lady
guess I'm here to stay
yes

crazy wisdom lady
crazy sunshine day
crazy wisdom lady
guess I'm here to stay

JOEL
That's fantastic! Are you really improvising that?

HATTIE
Yes, of course.

JOEL
Get the guitars!

JOEL *and* CHARLIE *take over the basic chord sequence and backing with great ease.* HATTIE *does scat singing, creative words—wildly so—at some point.*

CHARLIE
OK, I think we're a band; we are:

(Strikes a rock star pose, hits a big guitar chord)

Crazy Wisdom Lady!

JOEL
Ladies and Gentleman, welcome please, the wonderful, the amazing, the completely sensational Crazy Wisdom Lady band!

Hattie laughs her laugh.

CHARLIE
Yeah, nice dream.

HATTIE
Exactly!

INT. MADISON SQUARE GARDENS—NIGHT

Summer 1980. Spot on HATTIE *at grand piano. Sense and sound of substantial sized band, big percussion set, backing singers, the works. We only see* HATTIE. *Flowers. Classy piano. It could be a fantasy—fuzzy effects.*

ANNOUNCER
(American voiceover) Ladies and Gentlemen, let's have a huge New York welcome for the wonderful, the amazing, the completely sensational Crazy Wisdom Lady Band!

Opening bars of Crazy Wisdom Lady song, arranged with big backing sound and with audience applauding wildly as they recognise the opening chords.

Charlie: email

Not a movie

Hello dearest,

What can I possibly say in response to those scenes; memories so intense and sweet are flooding back moment by moment. What a shame we can't get smells into the script—that sandalwood oil you were wearing in the cinema that night—so exotic, so warm—that lemon tea that Joel was always making. Do you remember when his mother sent him a samovar? Worried he wasn't getting proper nourishment? I have lingered over those conversations in the kitchen, read them over and over again—marvelling at the happy chance that brought us all together. And then the music of course. How did we get that lucky? Perhaps the conversation in the bar is a little wordy, but good for a first draft. Did Joel write his own part there? Or did you?

I am also wondering about how best to write this. It was a lovely idea, a movie, and that's the only way actually that it can be told, this story of ours, the music, the foolery, the mystery. But the trouble is, it's not a film. Too many words. Long speeches. Show that to the money and they will run a mile. Even if you could get them to start talking, you'd have everyone else to worry about: a movie is subject to everyone's whim, gets endlessly rewritten, reshot, and cut up, and ends up nothing like anything you might have put in in the first place.

So, practically, no, it ain't a movie, and ought not to be, it's too valuable. So what is it, what will it be? Dunno. Let's keep writing it. Long speeches and all. It seems to work in movie format. If you write it as fiction, with an omniscient narrator, then the characters are not free, do you know what I mean? This way no-one gets to own the story. So let's let it follow its fortune and see what happens.

Love, dear

Joel, Hattie

Keep writing

—Hey Hattie.

—Joel—where have you been?

—Attending to things—you know.

—Yes. How good to have you back.

—Nice to be here. What are you writing? More of the film script?

—Yes—have you heard, though?—Charlie thinks it will never make a movie. Too much compromise with the money men needed in a film script, apparently.

—He knows what he's talking about. Important to get the story down on paper, though.

—Yes, that's what we're doing. I thought it would help us to keep some emotional distance by doing it as a script—less identification with the characters, if you see what I mean.

—Yes, of course. But are you sure it's a good idea to keep your distance?

—What do you mean, Joel?

—Well, just keep writing. Trust the process.

—You know something don't you.

—Don't you?

Charlie: email

Here you go, deferring

OK, here you go, my love: the five year old Hattie. Really you should write this, but you told it to me at a special time and I remember your telling so clearly. And in a way it's easier for me to create the five year old you. What do you think?

But actually what I am doing is deferring: to write about Joel is painful, so I'm avoiding it by imagining your past. It's a thing I do, I make a pastoral of the past, and duck into it and hide.

Your stuff is lovely, those sweet days...

Yes, you could come to Hammersmith, but actually I have space to get away and your place is so golden and enchanted, it seems right for this project to develop and grow in it. And with Charly not there, no (delightful) distractions.

Re the corridor: it's changed. I went to talk to the Drama Department a while ago, they were doing some nice community theatre work and asked for an ideas session. During a break I wandered down the English corridor, and was—appalled. There's now a thick deadening carpet, as beige as can be, and all the brightness has fallen out of the air.

The little bay has been walled in to make a room, so no more light. No more light. Ugh. Don't go there...

Love, dear.

xx

Charlie: filmscript 4

Gingerbread pig

INT. HATTIE'S PARENTS' HOUSE: HATTIE'S BEDROOM—EVENING

It's September 1954. HATTIE is five years old and sitting up in bed. FATHER (here in his late thirties) is sitting on bed. It's the nightly story time. HATTIE is about to start school next day, and it's a special story for starting school.

HATTIE
Story time, story time—what's the story tonight?

FATHER
Tonight's a really special story, because you're starting school tomorrow. Education is a wonderful thing, but you have to be careful with it.

HATTIE
What do you mean?

FATHER
Hattie, you're the brightest spark in my life, and what you'll find is, you're a lot cleverer than a lot of the people you'll come across as teachers. The thing is though, when you're little, you can't tell them that. Because they're the bosses. And what they will try to do is to make you less clever. But if you listen to the story and do what it says, then you'll have a way of dealing with this for the rest of your life: you'll be free.

HATTIE
Really?

FATHER
Yes, really—you know I never lie to you.

HATTIE
(Seriously) No, you never do.

FATHER
Right then. Now, you know the story of the Gingerbread Man?

HATTIE
Yes, boring.

FATHER
OK, clever-clogs—what's the story?

HATTIE
There's this *biscuit,* called the Gingerbread Man, and he keeps singing *(she sings)* 'Run, run, as fast as you can, you can't catch me, I'm the Gingerbread Man'. But they do catch him, and when they do they eat him, and serve him right for showing off like that.

FATHER
And you remember the story of the Three Little Pigs?

HATTIE
Yes, easy—*(big bad wolf voice)* 'Huff and puff and blow your house down'.

FATHER takes a gingerbread pig out of inside pocket and holds it up. It has a silver chain round its neck with a little silver pig hanging from it.

FATHER
Who do you think this is?

HATTIE
(Delighted) I don't know, who is he?

FATHER
This, my love, is the Gingerbread Pig.

HATTIE
No, no, you can't have a Gingerbread Pig, that's mixing up the stories.

FATHER
OK, Comrade Daughter, this is what you've got to learn: you have to learn

how to mix up the stories.

HATTIE
What does that mean, Dad?

FATHER
(Settling into story-telling mode) Listen to the story. Once upon a time, there was a Gingerbread Pig.

As the FATHER *tells the story, he picks up various toys and other objects from around the room for the characters, and puts them on* HATTIE's *bed. As she becomes engrossed in the story, visually she becomes part of the toy world, so the toys become characters, and the* FATHER's *voice is a voiceover.*

FATHER (V.O.)
And he knew three other pigs, whose names were Pig 1, Pig 2, and Pig 3. As pigs go, the three of them weren't very bright. So one day the Gingerbread Pig was having tea with Pig 1, who lived in a house made entirely of straw.

HATTIE
Why straw?

FATHER
I just told you—he wasn't very bright.

HATTIE
But it would let the rain in.

FATHER
It did. Be quiet for a bit.

HATTIE
I know the next bit: the big bad wolf comes along, and he says *(big bad wolf voice)* 'Huff and puff and blow the house down'.

FATHER
Right. And he does. And the Gingerbread Pig says to the big bad wolf: 'You can't eat us'. So the wolf says, 'Whyever not?' And the Gingerbread Pig says, 'Because we're Gingerbread Pigs'. 'So?' says the wolf. 'Well', says the Gingerbread Pig, 'wolves don't eat gingerbread, do they?' 'Oh' says the wolf, and sits down to think about it. And the Gingerbread Pig grabs Pig 1 by the trotter and runs off, singing *(he sings—he has a good voice)* 'Run, run, as fast as you can, they can't catch me I'm the Gingerbread Pig'; and they go to the house of Pig 2.

HATTIE

Made of wood, wasn't it?

FATHER

Yes, better for the rain.

HATTIE

No good against wolves though, was it?

HATTIE AND FATHER

(Together, in big bad wolf voices) 'Huff and puff and blow the house down'.

FATHER

So the Gingerbread Pig says to the big bad wolf: 'You can't eat us'. The wolf says, 'Whyever not?' And the Gingerbread Pig says, 'Because we're Gingerbread Pigs'. 'All of you?' says the wolf. 'Yes', says the Gingerbread Pig. 'And wolves don't eat gingerbread?' says the wolf. 'No', said the Gingerbread Pig. So the big bad wolf says 'Oh', and sits down to think about it. And the Gingerbread Pig grabs Pigs 1 and 2 by the trotter and runs off singing 'Run, run, as fast as you can, they can't catch me I'm the Gingerbread Pig'; and they go to the house of Pig 3.

HATTIE

And his house was made of brick.

FATHER

Right. He was a bourgeois pig. And he wouldn't let them come in.

HATTIE

(Amazed) Why not?

FATHER

He didn't believe in sharing. And he disapproved of Gingerbread Pigs.

HATTIE

He was really stupid.

FATHER

Right. But he did have a brick house. So the Gingerbread Pig said: 'Let us in, the big bad wolf is after us'. And Pig 3 said: 'What will you give me in return?' Because that's the way bourgeois pigs think.

HATTIE

They don't!

FATHER

Yes, believe it or not, they do. So the Gingerbread Pig said, 'We will give you solidarity and comradeship. Because you're going to need it.' And Pig 3 said, 'I don't think so'. So they went and hid behind a bush. Then up came the big bad wolf—

HATTIE

Huff puff?

FATHER

No, he wasn't that stupid. He said to Pig 3: 'Let me in, sir, and I'll give you a lot of money'. So Pig 3 said, 'Now we're talking,' and let him in. When the wolf was inside the brick house, Pig 3 said, 'Can I have my money now please?' And the wolf said, 'Shut up, it's rude to talk while you're being eaten'. So Pig 3 ran out of the door shouting 'Help help!' And there was the Gingerbread Pig, saying, 'What did you say?' 'Help help!' said Pig 3. And the Gingerbread Pig said: 'And what did I say to you not five minutes ago?' And Pig 3 said 'OK, you've made your point—now get me out of this'. Then up came the wolf, and he said, 'Right, come here, the four of you, you're dinner. And don't give me that crap about gingerbread, I don't care, I'm hungry.' So the Gingerbread Pig said, 'Could I just make a couple of points first?' 'Are they confusing?' said the wolf. 'No', said the Gingerbread Pig. 'OK then,' said the wolf, 'but be quick.' So the Gingerbread Pig said, 'Point one. Pigs have very sharp teeth and a strong bite. We crunch bones.' 'Do you?' said the wolf.

HATTIE

Do they?

FATHER

Yes. And the wolf said, 'Ah. And what's the second point?' 'The second point', said the Gingerbread Pig 'is that there are four of us and only one of you'. 'Oh', said the wolf. And the Gingerbread Pig took one step forward and looked fierce. Seeing this, Pigs 1 to 3 also took one step forward, and tried to look fierce. And the Gingerbread Pig said, very loudly, 'SO BUGGER OFF YOU FURRY FASCIST!' And the wolf let out a startled yelp: 'Eeeek!' and ran off.

And that's the story of the Gingerbread Pig.

Back to FATHER *and* HATTIE. *As the dialogue develops, we see how important the story is to him, and she sees this also.*

FATHER

Now, dear, what's that story about?

HATTIE

Solidarity forever?

FATHER

(Laughs) Yes my love, like all my stories; but what else is it about?

HATTIE

Wait a minute, there's something I don't understand. The other pigs say they're made of gingerbread. But they're not. It's a lie.

FATHER

Do you think the Gingerbread Pig is made of gingerbread? How can a pig be made of gingerbread?

HATTIE

So you mean, we are what we say we are?

FATHER

Yes, yes. We get to define ourselves. That is our right. No-one else has this right over us. Never forget that.

HATTIE

So when I'm at school, you mean I've got to tell people I'm a Gingerbread Pig? You don't mean that, do you?

FATHER

No. But what you'll find is, people will all the time try to tell you who you really are. They will say you're a good girl, or a bad girl, or top of the class, or number four in the class, or they don't like your accent, or you haven't got enough money, all sorts of things like that. And when they do any of that stuff, what you do is, you say to yourself, inside, secretly, 'They can't catch me I'm a Gingerbread Pig'.

In fact, the wise thing to do is to make them think you're just a little bit crazy. So they never know what you're doing to do next, because you never know what you're going to do next; that way you can't lose. So go to your school, enjoy the bits you can, laugh at the bits you can't, and together we'll make sure you get the best education possible right here with me and my books. Goodnight, Comrade Daughter.

He puts the pendant round her neck, and kisses her.

HATTIE
Goodnight Comrade Dad.

EXT. SCHOOL PLAYGROUND—MORNING

It's September 1959.

A primary school playground—the familiar Victorian building and sur-roundings. A boy is beating up a smaller boy. HATTIE, *who is half the bully's size, marches up behind him and taps him on the shoulder. He turns round.*

HATTIE

BUGGER OFF YOU FURRY FASCIST!

The boy's jaw drops. He is dumbfounded. She stamps on his foot. He bursts into tears. She marches off, proud of herself.

Hattie: email

Come and stay

WOW—I love it! You are the most extraordinary person—well—we know that dear Charlie—but you've really got Dad and that story... and I find myself liking little Hattie—and yes, you're right—much easier for you to do it than me! I'd forgotten I'd told you that story about the bully—how dear of you to remember.

Do come and stay here—it is heaven at this time of year. We could take over the little hut down at the water garden (I've just had a wood burning stove put in there) and plan to our hearts' content. I won't tell C you're coming, or she might refuse to go to Zurich!

I'd like you to hear the new songs—they're different. They're for a one-woman show that Jac's doing next year. And would you like to come and see Dad with me? He'd really like that.

And here I am avoiding writing about Joel to you.

Maybe remembering the past as pastoral is no bad thing, dear—it's like retroactive hope. And they were golden times, weren't they? They can destroy corridors, but they can't touch who we were, what we said, and what we did. Above all, what we knew.

I've nearly finished the next scenes—I'll attend to the day's early morning duties, meditate in the garden, drink my coffee, and then tidy them up and get them off to you before any more distractions arise.

love love love to you

H.

PS An email from Ariel Andrews dropped into my laptop this morning. Absolutely delightful and kind and warm and intelligent as ever. She was pleased to hear from us after all this time. How long is it, I wonder? I don't think I've been in touch since those hectic touring days—do you remember how we used to come across postcards in all sorts of unlikely places that squealed synchronicity at us, and gave us an excuse to write to her? That was fun, wasn't it? Anyway, she's not at the University at the moment; she's on a year's sabbatical, living in a rented cottage on the west coast of Ireland and writing something fictional. Apparently she's been having some success with playwriting, and now wants to see if she can pull a longish work of fiction together. So, no visit to us in the near future obviously. But she says she'd love to come and see us when she's back home—probably next August. Do you think it would be intrusive to ask her to read what we've written so far?

Hattie: email

Magical evening

Hello Charlie—here's that magical evening when I moved my stuff into the Beaumont/Cohen residence. It turned into a fantasy sequence part way through. Do you like it? I do. It sort of wrote itself that way—and seems to fit.

Hattie: filmscript 5

Singin' in the rain

EXT. CHARLIE'S HOUSE—EVENING

HATTIE is moving her stuff in. It's late October, 1970. Evening; darkness—light from street lights and windows and doorway of house. It's raining rather heavily—HATTIE and JOEL and CHARLIE are getting stuff out of a hired van, parked in the drive near the front door. They are rushing in

46

and out carrying a startling variety of objects into the well-lit and spacious hall. Trunks. Plants. Piles of colourful clothes—really beautiful. A Richard Lester scene.

JOEL

Hey, this is just like *Jules et Jim!* No—less angst, and more weather: it's *Singin' in the Rain.*

CHARLIE

Cue tap dance sequence . . .

He picks up an umbrella from the piles of HATTIE's *stuff that they are moving into the house, turns up his collar and moves into the 'Good morning, good morning' song from* Singin' in the Rain—*except he's singing 'Good evening good evening—we've worked the whole day through . . .'*

CHARLIE

Come on, I'll show you how to do it—it's easy.

HATTIE

I know it already: the working class does dance as well, you know.

JOEL

Well, you're going to have to show me!

HATTIE *and* CHARLIE *move into the well-lit hall doing a* Singin' in the Rain *type of sequence—they show* JOEL *what to do—he copies them—at first clumsily. Then we move into semi-fantasy—an immaculate tap routine— they are suddenly in full evening dress.* CHARLIE *is centre stage—*HATTIE *does a parody glamour girl act—letting* CHARLIE *and* JOEL *dance around her. In this fantasy,* JOEL *can dance well too.*

Hattie: email

How you two met

And here's one Joel and I did together—that conversation when I found out how you two met. OK? We need it in somewhere, don't we?

Hattie, Joel: filmscript 6

Rock climbing

INT. CHARLIE'S HOUSE: KITCHEN—EVENING

Winter 1970. HATTIE, JOEL, *and* CHARLIE *are sitting at the table*

HATTIE

How did you two meet, then?

CHARLIE

We both joined the University climbing club when we arrived. Seemed like a good idea at the time: get out of the city, into the hills, breathe the air. I'd done a little climbing at school...

JOEL

And so had I; so there we were, on the first trip to Wales. In the snow. In the mountains. It was really quite dangerous.

CHARLIE

And the problem was, the second year student who was supposed to be in charge didn't have the slightest idea.

HATTIE

What do you mean?

CHARLIE

Have you ever climbed?

HATTIE

No, strictly feet on the ground, that's me. Head in the sky, mind, but feet on the ground.

CHARLIE

OK, well, the main thing is, climbing is dangerous. You can get killed. And the way you guard against that is by following the rules, and by helping each other. So, if it gets dangerous, you rope up. Then, if one person falls, the others can dig an ice-axe into the snow or loop the rope around a bit of rock or something; you're not on your own, that's the thing: you help each other.

HATTIE

So on this trip?

JOEL

We were walking along a ridge across the head of a valley. Full of snow.

This turns into a voiceover—shots depicting the scene being described.

JOEL

One slip, and someone could have shot down that valley head first then over the edge. So Charlie said, 'We rope up now'. And the lad in charge said, 'Why bother, just to go across this little bit of a ridge?'.

There is a real edginess in this encounter—an implication from the lad in charge that CHARLIE is being weak and effeminate.

JOEL

And Charlie said, 'We rope up now'. He said it rather firmly. And I thought, 'That guy is not getting the message', so I came up behind and towered over him a little and brought the full weight of my ancestry to bear on the situation, including my mother's special look for dealing with idiots, and . . .

CHARLIE

And we roped up. No problem at all.

This is quickly spoken to gloss over the visual material which implies the lad in charge's antagonism to what he perceives as a gay man and a Jew—possibly even a gay man and a Jew in relationship with each other.

JOEL

And that was the beginning of a rather unlikely friendship: the actor and the rabbi.

CHARLIE

Have you heard the one about the actor and the rabbi?

Charlie: email

Free right now

Hey, wonderful! Almost too tantalising, getting it in instalments like this! Can't wait for the rest, tantrum, throw rattle out of cradle, more more, don't stop!

Listen, dearest, the current extravaganza has been put on hold: the female lead has broken her arm, poor dear, and since it's entirely funded on the basis of being her movie, the bean counters are running round in circles and flapping their wings pathetically. Looks most like a postponement until she's better. Just one of those stupid things: fell downstairs. And, clean as a whistle, too, no drugs or booze. How on earth did they get *Singin' in the Rain* insured, I parenthetically wonder? The insurance people must have had absolute faith in Donald O'Connor's talent. Amazing, that.

So, I'm free! Right now! No ties! Well, having said that, I'll untie what ties there are, and drive up (I'm in Hammersmith at the moment, in the flat), and get there before Charly's bed time tonight. Put in some beautiful time with her before she goes to Zurich and then we can work on the filmscript and have big ideas and wonderful times...

OK off to do some serious untying, see you real soon.

xxC

Hattie: email

Little C

How perfect! Thank you dear friend! I have to confess that little C guessed about you coming soon... must be something in my energy field that she picks up... where does she get that unasked-for talent from, I ask myself? And Zurich was seriously being re-considered—not a problem for us, we could have planned most things when she was asleep—but the good friends she's supposed to be travelling with (do you remember a band called Imperfect Pitch?—the woman who played alto sax with them lives up on the hill near here—and her little girl is C's best mate... tho not going to Zurich might have strained the connection a little!) Well, it would have disrupted the family somewhat... I did try and explain the ethical considerations to my gorgeous daughter, but she seemed to think her preference for being with you outweighed everything else under the sun. 'But he's my iftherewereaGodhe'dbemyGodfather' was her almost last parting shot... as she strode purposefully out of the kitchen door—turning in a dramatic pose that only you could have taught her and, sighing an agonised leading-lady sigh, shot the truly parting shot, 'This is my spiritual well-being at risk here.'

I didn't know whether to laugh or cry—so I laughed. I've told her you're almost on your way and she hasn't stopped jumping up and down... if only we could connect her up to the national grid, we could probably avoid the power cuts threatened for this winter.

So—I'm off to get extra special food to celebrate your imminent arrival. I'm waiting for Joel's opinion on the piece I just sent you before I do the next bit… I hope he's OK with it. And, it occurs to me to say, that if we work down in the water garden, he's likely to drop by every now and then—he likes it there too. Is that OK with you? No need to reply to that—just say honestly when you get here, and if you prefer we can work somewhere else.

lots of love dear Charlie

H.

Charlie: to a dictaphone

By the river

Sitting by the river that runs through Hattie's grounds. Funny, isn't it, to own a stretch of river. The moment of possession is the moment when you lose it. Come back, you're mine, oh dear, gone. And gone. And gone. Again and again forever. The power of it, the river, flowing unstoppably on. Just like being in love, really, isn't it? Just when you have sorted out a person to be in love with, gone, gone, she has gone, flowed past and vanished. All that is stable is the riverbed, the vehicle that constrains the flow. Which of course you never see, all you see is the mass of water, flowing always away.

Bloody hell, Charles, *mon petit charlatan,* what is this, a French movie?

Address the issue. The issue is this. It is, it is—unbearable, to spend so much time with Hattie. To sit and look at the red cloud of her hair, her animation, her certainty. The wild, gorgeous flow of ideas. Her musicality; how she lives all the time, I think, with roots in music, in a way that I can't really understand; somewhere always in her head there is a melody, a beat, a different drum.

The house is beautiful. A rambling mansion, multi-roomed, welcoming, in spacious grounds, acres of garden, the un-ownable river, woodland, the water garden. The autumn sunlight, golden in the golden trees. But that's not it. The animals and friends who live there, work there, are there, dogs and cats and horses. Little Charly, big dark eyes, bouncing and boundless, exquisite child. All that, so much, and that's not it, either. Not it. It is what you feel when you come up the drive. It is: the feeling of flying close to the sun, towards the limit of what's bearable; closer, closer, wanting to turn round and drive right back down to the little road that leads to the bigger road that leads to London, normality, things I can handle. Oho, Charlot, exaggerating again, another song and dance act, is it? No. It is not. To be there is to swim in fire. It is to know, to know, as she knows, that you must go through the fire to the light. And, in my case, knowing that, to hold back.

And all the time as well as that there is all the rest: the music, laughter, stories, pure pleasure. This song and dance act, and all that. Pratfalls, acrobatics. Joy, real joy, also. Her incredible laughter. But knowing too that the only way forward is to dive into the sun. To be utterly consumed, not a scrap left over, greasepaint, clown suit, parping horn, red nose, utterly eaten up by fire. Goodbye, Charlie. And not to be able to do that.

Hattie: journal

When you write a song

We were sitting together, the three of us, in the music room. It was a golden late summer day. I was playing a new song for big Charlie and he was sitting beside me on the piano stool—adding bits and playing the fool a little. Well, a lot actually. I remember laughing. Little Charly looked across from her place in the window seat and said: 'When you write a song, where does the music come from?' In the stillness that followed the question, when big Charlie and I were holding our breath with wonder, we heard a skylark singing and saw it fly high above the woods beyond the kitchen garden.

She laughed and pointed and ran out of the room into the garden, not needing us to speak the answer. We held each other and wept with joy.

Hattie: email

Thank you

Charlie—what can I say? Thank you so much for last week. Magical, perfect, blissfully happy.

The house seems empty without you. Little C has bubbled off to school—it's good to have her home. Thank you dear friend for waiting for her to get back from Switzerland. The look on her face when she saw you in the kitchen is something I'll never forget! I do hope she doesn't lose all this joy as she grows up.

Strange that it's nearly November—Later today, I'm hoping to write that November 5th conversation that we had when I first moved into the Edgbaston house—out of sequence I know, but it feels the perfect piece to write today.

Hope you had an easy ride home to the big Tomato (Little C says it's like the big Apple only squishier. I said it's like the big Apple only with less bite to it).

More soon—things to do. Love Hattie

Charlie: email

You say tomato

Hello dear heart

Yes, it was wonderful, I am still there, also here, covered in tomato sauce. London as horror movie, fake gore. They are trying yet again to make me break my vow never to go near telly, and I am resisting, with vigour. Shakespeare's clowns. damn it, it sounds good, too, doesn't it? I'm doing some Cathar research, more anon, my love, my dear.

xxC

Hattie: email

enjoy

Here you are dear. Enjoy!

Love always H.

Hattie: filmscript 7

Charlie's story

INT. CHARLIE'S HOUSE: KITCHEN—EVENING

CHARLIE and HATTIE are sharing a pot of tea at the big table. It is Friday evening—the one before November 5th. Outside the big window, they can see bonfire parties in other people's gardens, fireworks. They are looking out of the window and seeing next door's garden party—lots of kids, kids' noises—a burning Guy.

HATTIE

My Dad taught me not to get too enthusiastic about bonfire night.

CHARLIE

Why? Too right-wing?

HATTIE

He disapproves of torture.

CHARLIE

Torture? Bonfire night?

HATTIE

Guy Fawkes was arrested for being involved in a Catholic plot to blow up the House of Commons with the king in it. He was tortured very cruelly. He lasted for a long time before he gave up his co-conspirators. Then they burned him alive. It seems a strange thing to encourage children to celebrate.

CHARLIE

Christ I'd never thought about it like that. Your father really worked at your education, didn't he? You're very lucky.

HATTIE

My father is a great man. He believes you should watch yourself all the time, and not take anything for granted.

JOEL comes into doorway dressed in a suit, a very smart coat, a proper hat over his yarmulke.

JOEL

Sorry to be going out on your first proper night here, but Friday night is Friday night, and there are three stars in the sky.

CHARLIE

Are you coming back to eat, or is one of those Jewish mothers going to force-feed you again?

JOEL

It's one of the benefits of being so thin, don't knock it. It's Mrs. Silverstein's turn tonight. At least she hasn't got a daughter, and, actually, I have to say, her chicken soup, well, whole food it isn't, but it really is good. And reminds me of what it was like to be 5 years old. Which is nice in its way.

CHARLIE

OK—enjoy—see you later.

SYNAGOGUE

Friday night service—very moving and musical and exotic. It's an orthodox service. There is richness of colour and texture and sound. JOEL is taking a central part in the service because he is knowledgeable and experienced. Lots of shots from the ladies' gallery as different mothers watch him admiringly as a potential husband for their daughters.

THE SILVERSTEINS' DINING ROOM

A big table with about 12 people round it, white cloth, wine, wine glasses, Friday night plaited loaves (2) covered with a white cloth. The table is laid impeccably. Lots of little shots of people filling up JOEL's plate—lots of food, lots of generosity. Chicken soup—then chicken. A bit helter skelter and quite funny.

But after the meal come the Friday night songs. The pace slows right down. The song that lingers is very very beautiful—exquisite harmonies. Depth and beauty.

We have subtitles to explain the Hebrew.

Hi-neh mah tov u-ma na-im

She-vet a-chim gam ya-chad

(Behold how good and how pleasant it is for brothers and sisters to dwell together in unity)

Camera has been behind JOEL—moves to focus on his face—he has tears running down his face.

CHARLIE'S HOUSE: KITCHEN.

HATTIE *and* CHARLIE *are closing the window, drawing the curtains. We can still just hear the noise of fireworks and party from outside.*

CHARLIE

Right, brown rice then, is it?

HATTIE

Fuck that, let's get some fish and chips.

LATER

They are in a room which is the opposite of the Silverstein dining room. A big empty room, which was once a grand dining room. CHARLIE doesn't use it—the house has more than enough rooms—and eating usually takes place in warmer, cosier places. They have a trestle table like the ones you use for wall papering and upturned storage boxes to sit on. Candlelight, soft rock music, family silverware and china, cut glass goblets, a litre of vin de table. It's cold, so they've brought in some electric fires. CHARLIE has several sweaters on and a big woolly scarf. HATTIE is wrapped in a gorgeous blanket.

HATTIE

You can always trust a wine where you have to unscrew the top, in my opinion.

CHARLIE

Yes, unpretentious but stunningly robust. Rather like you, actually.

HATTIE

(Laughs)

Whereas you are chateau bottled, *appellation contrôlée,* and certainly *premier cru.* But I don't have the bouquet yet, and I want to know: tell me about you.

CHARLIE

OK. I'm an actor: I can act me.

HATTIE

Right, that's a start.

CHARLIE

I can act anything: historical-pastoral, tragical-historical, scene individable, or poem unlimited. *Especially* poem unlimited.

HATTIE

OK, shut up now and listen. I understand Joel because I know a bit about the Jewish thing and I understand outsiders. But the ones I really don't understand, and really don't trust, are the people who went to public schools. The ruling class. I was trained to be very wary of people like you. But I know that you are going to be my lifelong friend. So I need to bridge that gap. OK: do it. Give me the *cinema verité*.

We go into black and white Georgie Girl *atmosphere.* CHARLIE *rushes around (speeded up) arranging the set, turns the room into a mess. There is a big cupboard in the corner–he pulls out all sorts of stuff till it becomes a set for* Look back in Anger. HATTIE *gets it straight away–starts ironing.*

CHARLIE (CONT'D)
(looking through pile of LPs)

I'm sure I've got the sound effect of bloody bells somewhere, I used it in a production.

He finds it.

CHARLIE (CONT'D)
Yes!

He puts it on the gramophone

BELL RINGING NOISES

CHARLIE *strikes Jimmy Porter attitude*

CHARLIE (CONT'D)
Christ those bloody bells. Leave out the squirrels!

HATTIE
Oh just a little 'does my huffy bunny want to play with his little squirrel?'

CHARLIE
Oh for Christ's sake.

They both laugh. They both pull yuk faces.

Close-up of HATTIE's *face; now back in colour.*

HATTIE
(Serious and kindly)

I really do want to know.

She picks up a candle in a candlestick and two wine glasses full of wine and goes out of French windows into the darkness of the garden.

It's a dark night. They sit at an old garden table. CHARLIE *has brought a candlestick out here too. Their faces are lit softly by the candlelight.*

HATTIE
It must hurt a lot.

CHARLIE
You can tell?

HATTIE
Yes I can tell. I thought the workers had the monopoly on that kind of anguish.

CHARLIE
Anguish has nothing to do with money. Everyone suffers: everyone.

Hattie: email

Your words

Dearest—I think you have to take the script from here, don't you? Funnily enough, your words and gestures and the whole ambience of that night-time conversation are as clear to me as if they happened yesterday, but it feels right that you should tell the next bit.

love as always H

Charlie: email

You're right

Yes. You're right. I'm sure you could have done this perfectly, but it's good that I should have pulled it together here. Thank you for listening and understanding—then and now. What is this we're doing here? Well, whatever, I'm glad we're doing it.

Love to you my love

Charlie

Charlie: filmscript 8

Charlie's story continued

CHARLIE

See, what you have to understand is, I got the basic training. The full thing. My education was designed to create leaders. Generals, captains of industry, Tory politicians, that kind of thing: people who have real power. People who can send thousands of men into battle to die, or lay off thousands of workers: very hard people. They train you to do that by throwing the book at you. They give you hell from an early age. I left home when I was 9. Prep school, public school. Running with the wolves. It was wicked, what those boys did to each other, what we did to each other; and they encouraged it, because they knew it created people who could make people do what they wanted. Who could play the game of power, without compunction or hesitation. The bullying was unspeakable. The cruelty was on a daily basis. You had to handle it; you had no choice. As a result, you acquired a very hard surface, a brilliant diamond-like hardness. You could handle anything that life threw at you, and you could cut through it all. Problem, though: somewhere along the line, feeling went out of the window. That too was part of the plan: you can't send soldiers into battle to die if you can feel. So, inside the diamond, ice. No feelings.

I found out how to act a part: I found out I could do that. And I found that as long as I acted, I was safe. I could make people laugh.

HATTIE

OK, I understand how you coped: but what allowed the ice to melt?

CHARLIE

Once I turned into a clown, it got better. And when I found out that I was good at running, distance running, it got better still. They all thought I was running to compete, but actually I wasn't in the competition at all; I ran and ran, but I was running away.

HATTIE

What do you mean?

CHARLIE

When I ran I would go into my own private world, where none of it mattered; there was nothing but running, I could stop thinking, I could be free. The loneliness of the long-distance clown, you might say.

HATTIE
Did you never think of just running away? Seems like the obvious thing to do.

CHARLIE
Well, yes; I did. Actually, I walked.

HATTIE
Tell me about it.

Voiceover from here: we see what he is talking about.

CHARLIE (V.O.)
Well, I was 15. Mother was taking me back after the Easter holiday. She didn't want to leave me there, and I didn't want to leave her, and the tension in the car was extreme. There'd been a row at home, I'd tried to persuade my father to let me go to an ordinary school and he thought I was mad. And I knew that when I went through those school gates I would turn into the person I was in that place, and I hated it. So when Olivia dropped me off, and just drove away because she couldn't think of anything else to do, I left my bag in the street, and walked, and kept on walking, right past the gates, and straight on and on. I walked for six hours. I have no recollection of any of it. I was completely on the edge, in deep deep despair; I could see nothing but greyness.

HATTIE
And then?

CHARLIE
The next couple of days are a blur. I didn't eat. I don't think I slept, or maybe I slept a lot, I have no idea. I have a vague memory of being driven in a car by a man with a foreign accent, but I could have dreamt or hallucinated that. But somehow I ended up in Edinburgh, of all places. By that time of course they were searching for me all over, but I didn't even think of that. I was mad, Hattie; I was quite mad.

She reaches out and touches him.

HATTIE
Are you OK telling me this, do you want to stop?

CHARLIE
No. I want to tell you.

CHARLIE (V.O.)

The first clear memory I have after that grey nightmare time is, I was sitting under a railway bridge, by the river. I'd come across a community of people who were sleeping rough. They accepted me just the way I was, they neither welcomed me nor rejected me, they just let me be. Nobody there had anything at all to lose, they were right at the bottom. They had no curiosity, desire, or expectation. So they were free, you see, and I felt at home.

With the voiceover, we see:

CHARLIE *among the tramps. Under a bridge, twilight, fire in a can with holes in it, everyone just sitting. Some have bottles. Wrapped up in old coats. Dog-ends passed around. Occasional noises: mad laughter, or groans. It is hell.* CHARLIE *is thin and wasted and white as a sheet and shaking slightly. He is looking at nothing.*

Camera on his face, darkness increasing. Then he blinks, and notices that the bundle of rags next to him is in distress. Stertorous breathing, rather desperate. He looks. It's a tramp, old, utterly ravaged. Somehow CHARLIE *wakes up enough to realise that this man needs help. You can see the fog clearing a little in his eyes.*

CHARLIE

Are you OK?

The man says nothing. Breathing is getting worse. Charlie reaches across and takes the man's hand; the man grips his hand hard.

CHARLIE (V.O.)

I looked at him, and thought: this man needs help. This is the first thought I'd had for a long time. But I didn't know how to help him. And then I knew, I just knew, there was nothing I could do; that he was dying. I looked at him, and, Hattie, this is it: I knew something else as well. I knew he was OK. I knew he was doing the right thing, and I knew that he knew it too. There we were, together, locked in a shared moment, surrounded by that terrible no-hope madness, and it was fine. In fact, it was perfect. It was perfect. And what I knew, knew deep down with the utmost certainty, was that he was me. I was him. There was no barrier between us; there was just one being there. And because of that, everything was absolutely fine. We must have stayed like that through the night, because I can remember it getting dark and quiet, and then later the dawn breaking, but to me it seemed like minutes. I felt it when he left. He left with the first sunshine. He took one deep breath in, and I thought he was going to say something, but in fact that was it; he left. But I stayed holding his hand through the morning. Then I left too. I got up and walked away and came to a phone box and called my mother.

HATTIE

What an amazing gift, how lucky you were to receive it.

End of V.O. CHARLIE *looks at* HATTIE *with surprise, admiration, relief.*

CHARLIE

You know you're the first person who's understood that without me having to explain it; you understood straight away, didn't you?

HATTIE

Yes of course.

CHARLIE

So then I called my mother and life started again.

There is companionable silence—night time garden noise in the dim light. Together they snuff the candles out. Sound of garden in the darkness.

November 2003

Charly: blog

I am Charly

Hi, this is me! Me! Strange word, is me. My cat Jeffrey says me, me, says it a lot. Especially when hungry, which is more than sometimes. He is a me cat. I am Charly. Charlie is Charly too. Only we spell it different otherwise we would be the same. I think this is wonderful. Joel agrees. Don't you, Joel?

—Yes, dear.

—Are you my father, Joel?

—Yes, my love.

—And Charlie, he is my father too, isn't he?

—Of course he is.

—And Grandad, especially?

—Of course.

—You are very wise Joel. You are wise like Jeffrey. He sleeps a lot.

—Wise.

—I think so.

Anyway, this is my weblog. My blog. It is a blog of one, only I read it. I write to me. And Joel, of course.

Today I went and talked to my horse, she is called Ayesha. She is an Arab. She is as beautiful as God. I saw her born, Mum pulled her out. Awesome. Awesome, is my Mum. All night it took, I stayed up. I was a bit scared but Joel was kind like always. Mum said, learn; blood, birth, learn. She is awesome tough, is my Mum. I think I learned, I prayed, I hope that helped. Did I learn, dear Joel?

—I think so, dear Charly.

Anyway Charlie is teaching me many many things. He teaches me to fight. Haaa! He says, and haaa! I say, and we hit and block. I kicked him in the golden target yesterday and he had to go and recover, Mum laughed like a waterfall. I didn't mean to, but it happened. He should of blocked but was not quick. I was quick. Woo! Well, Murray taught me secretly. Charlie came back wearing a dustbin lid. Clank!

Zurich was beautiful but not as beautiful as Ayesha. The lake is nice. The town is white and nice and the lake is blue and the mountains are reasonably awesome. I can speak German! A bit. Hey Joel *wie geht's mein herr?*

—*Nu, to zayt mir gezunt!*

—You speak funny German.

—My grandparents. They were funny Germans.

—Goodbye blog for now. *Wiedersehen* Mr Joel.

—*Shalom mein liebling.*

Charly: blog

Love and work

Hi, blog, me again. Today was good. Though wet. I am making a movie with my friend Annabel Atkinson. She is the star, and I am the star also. Charlie gave me a little matchbox movie camera, and I must make a matchbox movie with it. Mum says always you must honour the gift. With what? With work. With love and work. What else? she says. It is called angels by the lake.

Obviously is a very good word. Everything should be more obviously.

You can't really see the angels but you know they are there.

My friend Simon teaches me the piano. He comes down for the day and we do things, it is so nice. He teaches me to get into the groove also. The groove is better than perfect, and easier, also harder. It is very obviously. Sometimes I can do it, now, the groove, and every time Mum knows, wherever she is in the house, and often comes and smiles, maybe does backing vocals a little. When you are in the groove people smile, Simon says. Mum says, the house smiles.

Simon is a trainee blissmaster. He is so cool. He can clown too, but not like Charlie. Charlie can clown like an angel, except you can see him easily.

Annabel said to me, when we first met, why don't I look like my mother? But I do, I said. No you don't, she said, you have brown skin and slanty eyes and black hair. Yes, I said, just like my mother. Who died. Died? she said, she looked pale and worried. Yes, in the high snow valley, the Chinese shot her, with an aeroplane, she was walking to India. Oh, she said, in a little small voice. And Rinpoche came, didn't he, Joel? He came out of his retreat, down from the mountain, because he knew. And he carried me instead, all the way to India, through the high snow valleys, through the cold. He kept me warm. He knows the heat practice. Ooo, the warmth, I remember that. And my mother had finished with her body so she gave it to the birds, that is our custom, and now she is buried in the sky. And Rinpoche did the Poa for her, walking through the snow, so now she is in Dewachen. Oh, Annabel, I said, don't cry, don't cry, and I cried a bit too, but it was only a very little bit, wasn't it, Joel, and we were best friends after that.

So that's why I look different from my Mum but the same as my mother. And Rinpoche came to the west with me, and he went on, to Boulder Colorado, to the wild west, he said, laughing, oh you should hear him laugh (if a blog could hear): I am in the wild west, he said, with all the wild westerners, and I teach them how to be even more wild, he said, laughing and laughing, laughing like a big river, because that is how it is, to be free. Free and clear, he says: free and clear. And sometimes, a lot, when I go to sleep, I am still in his arms, hearing him quietly chanting, steadily walking always, crump crump crump in the snow, and I can feel the heat, the heat of his heart.

I am Rinchen. It means precious jewel. And I am Charly too, because I asked him, Charlie, for his name, as a gift, for my birthday. It was the best gift. So all the time I earn it, because you must earn every gift, says Mum, with love and work. And when she talks like that, with that nearfaraway voice, you do it, whatever it is, you just do it. I earn it with backflips and snapkicks and tai chi and foolery and sitting, quiet, quiet. And I love him.

Charly, Joel

Midrash kinderlach

—Do you have a blog Joel?

—No *kinderlach*—do you think it would be a good idea?

—Yes.

—Why?

—Then I could read it and I'd know more.

—You know you can always ask me anything you want to, don't you?

—Yes, but supposing you know something—something really important and I never get to think of asking the right question? If you blogged some then I could get surprise knowing.

—That makes sense. I'm not sure blogging is the easiest way to do it though.

—Well—please think of something Joel. I think it's quite important. Get your people to call my people.

—Your people shall be my people, sweetheart. And wherever you go I will go.

—That's nice Joel.

—It's a *midrash, kinderlach.*

—What's a *midrash*?

—It comes from the Hebrew word that means 'to seek' or 'to enquire'.

—Do I *midrash* Joel?

—Definitely darling. Definitely.

—OK. That's cool. That's a bloggy thing.

Charly: blog

Mum told me a story

Mum told me a story. It was big. She said, like she does, Charly, would you like a story? Obviously, I said, totally obviously. Well, I nearly said it, but my mouth tripped up. We were sitting by the big fire. She was looking at the fire. She told me this story, and I am writing it down so that I will never never forget it.

A long time ago. There was a castle; turrets and battlements and troubadours and ladies and jousts, there were jousts, and chivalry, all those lovely words, that lovely world. And they all spoke a beautiful lost language, that sounds like a songbird, birdsong. It was heavenly, I think. There was a troubadour who was a singer, a singer of stories and songs. His name was—

—Charlie! I said, and she looked at me, farNearly, and happySadly, too. And then she said some words in the songbird language, and told me his name, a birdsong name. There was a Lady, she said, and he loved her. And then she kissed me, with bright eyes, and there was a tear running all the way down her cheek. It was salty. And then I went to bed, because she said she would tell me the whole story, bit by bit, and she will.

Hattie: email

Exquisite

Hello Charlie

This piece came out of nowhere yesterday when I was sitting by the fire in the music room with little C. I wrote it down straight away. Do you think it works? Is anyone going to understand this?

Little C knew. Knows. Are you doing OK? Are you busy writing? Stay in touch please. This is exquisite and exquisitely painful too.

All love to you. Hattie.

Hattie: filmscript 10

Troubadour

EXT. CASTLE GARDEN—MORNING

It is the twelfth century.

NB Same actor plays HATTIE/BEATRITZ. *Same actor plays* CHARLIE/TROUBADOUR. *In a later scene the* JOEL *actor plays the* PARFAIT.

This scene is played and shot realistically: it is not a fantasy sequence. It is important that these events are established as a historical reality, not a dream.

A formal garden in castle grounds.

The camera follows the criss-crossing paths and comes to a fountain.

The LADY *is sitting in a circular arbour, on a bench. It's springtime—spring flowers, fresh and green. We can see mountains in the distance: the Pyrenees—snow and sunlight on them.*

*Sound of the lark—*BEATRITZ *sings the same melody as the lark; just the melody. She is richly dressed, so that it's obvious to the incoming* TROUBADOUR *that she is the* LADY *of the house.*

The TROUBADOUR *approaches confidently, looking about him. He is carrying a lute.*

TROUBADOUR

(Bows. Speaks formally)

Lady, I do not know which to prefer: the song of the skylark, or the voice that comes after.

BEATRITZ

Sir, I think you flatter me—but you do it rather well.

TROUBADOUR

Lady, that is what I do for a living.

BEATRITZ

(She laughs HATTIE's *laugh)*

Are you newly come to my husband's court?

TROUBADOUR

Yes, Lady. Last night I slept in Quillan.

BEATRITZ

You have travelled far in a day: why do you come here?

TROUBADOUR

Because I heard from afar of your beauty and your songs. And besides, I'm rather short of money at the moment, and your husband's generosity is famous.

BEATRITZ

It's true: a nicely turned set of compliments to me will earn you food and wine and a place to stay for as long as you wish.

TROUBADOUR
Your beauty grows more amazing by the minute, Lady.

BEATRITZ
So they tell me. Frequently. However, that interests me not in the least. I am interested in poetry.

TROUBADOUR
Well, that's a relief. What would you like to know about poetry? I have studied little else since I became a man.

BEATRITZ
Not as a boy?

TROUBADOUR
Poetry is not for children, Lady.

BEATRITZ
Is poetry for women, sir?

TROUBADOUR
Without my lover I would have no poetry.

BEATRITZ
What is her name?

TROUBADOUR
I may not speak her name.

BEATRITZ
Where did you meet her?

TROUBADOUR
I meet her daily, in only one place: a dream, a garden, a song. We call it the *loc aizi*, the beautiful place.

BEATRITZ
I have heard my father speak of this. Where is it?

TROUBADOUR
Lady, it is here.

BEATRITZ
Are we in it now?

TROUBADOUR
No, we are not.

BEATRITZ

How can it be here if we are not in it?

TROUBADOUR

Ask the skylark.

Sound of skylark. We see the bird spiralling upward in the sky towards the sun.

CASTLE: BEATRITZ' MUSIC ROOM

A small room—fire in fireplace—small table—2 chairs—quite intimate. There is a window with a view of the mountains—snow on top. The PARFAIT and BEATRITZ are standing for main part of the conversation. He is wearing a plain dark black robe.

BEATRITZ

Please help me.

PARFAIT

I have prepared your medicine, Lady; I have also given you the words to say and the pictures to make in your mind. These will help you to be well; when you are well, then a child will come, or not, I cannot say.

BEATRITZ

But you were brought here to help me conceive. You are famous for your healing arts. My husband summoned you here to provide him with an heir.

PARFAIT

Lady, I am bound to tell the truth. I will do my best to make you well, but I cannot happily bring a child into the place of suffering.

BEATRITZ

Where is this place of suffering?

PARFAIT

It is here.

BEATRITZ

Are we in this place of suffering?

PARFAIT

Yes, Lady, we are in hell.

BEATRITZ

How do we get out of it?

PARFAIT
Lady, ask the skylark.

BEATRITZ
I would rather ask you.

They sit together at the table for a formal teaching—camera and sound pull away from them—we see their heads close together—they are locked in an intense and animated discussion—no hint of sensuality.

Charly, Joel

Jewish inside

—Hello Joel.

—Hello *kinderlach.*

—Why do you speak such funny German Joel?

—It's not really German at all dear one—it's Yiddish.

—You mean like Jewish people used to speak?

—Yes—like your friend Miriam's family do.

—I like them. They smile crinkly and look at you straight in the eyes and deep inside. Are you Jewish Joel?

—In a way. I used to be.

—Like I used to be Tibetan?

—In a way. I stay sort of Jewish inside.

—Is it good inside?

—It's not good not bad now. It used to hurt quite a lot I remember.

—Did you cry when it hurt?

—Yes, *kinderlach.* Yes, I cried.

—Me too. Sometimes. But you know that don't you Joel.

—Yes, I do.

—Do you know everything Joel?

Charly: blog

The Following Cat

I have been talking to my cat Jeffrey. Mum says he is a poem and I think so too. Charlie calls him the Following Cat, because he does. Mum comes into the big living room to play the piano, and after her comes the Following Cat. I was telling him about the Dharma. Simon has started to teach me the Dharma. Rinpoche rang him up and said it is time. He will teach me the letters, the beautiful holy letters that hang from a line like prayer flags, but first he is teaching me to watch the mind. This is easy. It is easy to sit quietly and feel the inner warmth and the arising of compassion, I have always done that, I think Rinpoche gave it to me, carrying me in his arms. Or maybe I had it before. So I sit and the funny me voice bounces around for a while and then not so much, and then I am in the groove, smiling, and the house smiles. And maybe Mum will feel the house smile and come in and smile too, and maybe sit for a while quietly too. But today the Following Cat came in, and I explained to him that he had to watch the breath coming in and out of his nose, and he started to purr, which is maybe the same thing. And I told him he must not criticise the me mind, he must love it, or it won't settle down, and he opened his eyes and looked at me, the cat look, as if I was really really stupid, and then closed his eyes and I closed my eyes and we had a really nice time, smiling both.

Joel, Charly

Joel's blog

—Hey *kinderlach* guess who?

—Hey Mr Joel!

—Got it in one *wunderkind.*

—Can I be a *wunderkinderlach*?

—Oh yes—could you be anything else? Come into my *kindergarten wunderkinderlach.*

—Have you got a garden Joel?

—Darling. I am a garden.

—A garden or THE garden.

—Good question. I'll blog you on that.

—But you don't have a blog. Do you Joel?

—Well, I sort of do now.

—What do you mean?

—Well, I can blog but I don't use the World Wide Web.

—What DO you use?

—Indra's net, darling girl.

—Did you mean the internet Joel?

—No—listen carefully—Indra's net.

—Wow—what's that?

—Ask your World Wide Web *kinderlach*. Ask the World Wide Web.

Charly, Hattie

Indra's Net

—Mum, do you know what Indra's net is?

—Yes, dear. Is this for school?

—No, it's for Joel.

—But Joel knows what Indra's net is.

—Yes, I know he does, but he's told me to find out, and so I am doing.

—Ah. Did he give you any clues?

—Well, he says he can do blogging on it and doesn't need the World Wide Web.

—Oh I see what he means.

—Do you? Can I do it too? Can I?

—Yes dear.

—When?

Charly, Joel

Charlie's calls

—OK Mr Joel. I totally get the Indra's net thing. Are you there?

—Always.

—Do you always answer—whoever's calling?

—No dear—I screen calls. I always answer you. But you know that don't you?

—Yes Joel, I do. Do you always answer Mum's calls?

—Of course—we talk a lot. We do lots together too.

—And Charlie's calls?

—Charlie doesn't call me.

—Why not?

—Perhaps you could ask him that?

—Are you saying that because you don't know the answer?

—No.

—Are you saying that because you don't want to tell me something?

—No. Think again little one.

—Will it be kind to Charlie if I ask him?

—*Wunderbar wunderkind.*

—I love you Joel.

December 2003

Charlie: email

Down to earth scenes

Here we are, dear—at last—I hear you cry. Sorry for a bit of a gap. Got lost in the twelfth century somewhere in too much research. A lot of mud to get stuck in—wheels spinning wildly to no avail. Have given self severe reprimand for trying to be too clever. Too academic. Was so touched by your piece that surfaced for the dear child—the Troubadour and the Lady—and wanted to come back to you with something similar, but I think perhaps you should be the one to put those strange magical dreamlike scenes on paper. You and Joel too, maybe? I can't capture the style. And your Toulouse experience was the start of all our collective dreaming. The catalyst. I think you have the gift.

Anyway, here are some more down to earth scenes which I quite like. I think. Be honest in your response though. Utterly willing to write and rewrite and rework whatever needs doing.

Herewith and without further ado (except this self indulgent bit of patter) but with trumpets sounding

1. The graduation party and the Ariel Andrews conversation

2. The wedding and the sweet stuff with Mildred (My God you were stunning in that part my love)

I'll tuck those rediscovered scenes of Joel's in in the middle of these scenes of mine. So you can read them together and see if they fit. I've edited the layout a bit in transcribing them. It makes logical sense to put them together, but artistically we might want something to intervene in the final version. More Provençal material perhaps?

3. The chat with my dear paternal Grandfather. I hope I've done him justice. I've had to make him slightly less taciturn than in real life—I understood his truncated utterances and graphic gestures, but I'm not sure they'd make much sense to anyone else. We are thinking of showing this to the world aren't we? If not as a movie, then as a book maybe?

Must go now—a meeting with my new PA. Hilary d'Angelo; Bodyguard to the Stars. Nothing like a Roedean education is there? I am safe at last.

Tell little C that I'm working on that idea for a double act that she sent me, and that I think it's a sure-fire winner. Does she want to be the front end or the back? Her wish is my command. Suit has been ordered and will be arriving from the theatrical costumiers within the fortnight hence.

Away away—much love as always.

Charlie.

Charlie: filmscript 11

Ariel Andrews

EXT. THE UNIVERSITY: LAWN OUTSIDE ARTS FACULTY—AFTERNOON

June 1971. Garden party after graduation ceremony. Camera high up looking down—milling throng, academic dress, parents in suits and silly floral frocks, silly hats. Some students in protest dress with their gowns—jeans, colourful long dresses, etc.

Camera weaves round as we overhear snatches of conversation to establish the nature of the event: graduation.

WOMAN 1

You must be so proud of Melissa.

WOMAN 2

Yes we always knew she had it in her.

WOMAN 3

And are you a graduate yourself?

MAN 1

Yes I was at Queen Mary's in the early days—maths, though. Nothing fancy like this. Never quite understood why anyone would want to study English literature.

MAN 2
Bloody hell, hope this doesn't go on too much longer, I need a proper drink.

MAN 3
Me too. Still, it's nice for the kids.

KID 1
Christ this is boring.

KID 2
Yes, but it's nice for the parents.

KID 1
Maybe.

Small chamber orchestra is playing something classical and nondescript. We home in on HATTIE, CHARLIE, *and* JOEL.

CHARLIE
That violinist is bored to death.

HATTIE
So am I. Let's get the hell out of here.

JOEL
Lucky we insisted our parents didn't come.

HATTIE
Correction: my father insisted on not coming.

CHARLIE
OK let's go: let's get a bus into town and find a movie.

They are heading towards freedom, walking across the grass. ARIEL ANDREWS *accosts them.*

ARIEL ANDREWS
Where are you going? I need someone to talk to.

CHARLIE
Sorry, we can't stand it.

ARIEL ANDREWS
I can't stand it either: come and have a drink with me: I've got a bottle of good wine in my room.

INT. THE UNIVERSITY: ARIEL ANDREWS' ROOM—MOMENTS LATER

Messy cheerful university room. Books. Papers. Interesting pictures on wall. Tree in full summer leaf outside window. Sounds of garden party going on outside.

ARIEL ANDREWS

OK, I'm getting the plane to Zurich at half past five, the taxi is coming at 3.30.

She pours wine into four glasses and hands them around.

JOEL

What are you doing in Zurich?

ARIEL ANDREWS

Summer course at the Jung Institute—I go most years.

HATTIE

Wow, fantastic.

ARIEL ANDREWS

Here, have a look at the programme.

She passes it over. They all look at it.

CHARLIE

Hey, that sounds really good.

He quotes titles of a couple of sessions.

Insert titles in German maybe?

JOEL

Have you read the new biography?

ARIEL ANDREWS

Yes, what did you think?

JOEL

Too much gossip, not enough theory.

ARIEL ANDREWS

God, I'm going to miss you three. Look, stay in touch, will you? A letter from time to time? Something like that?

HATTIE

Yes. We will. We owe you. And in fact we're staying in Birmingham, so we could meet up some time maybe, compare notes?

ARIEL ANDREWS

Sure. What are you going to do?

CHARLIE

I've decided to take a walk-on part at the RSC. Their autumn production of *The Tempest*. It was either that or a radio soap. A tough choice—but the Bard won.

HATTIE

I've got a job in BBC radio. Assistant researcher—current affairs. I'm going to work my way up as fast as I can, and make the programme of my dreams.

ARIEL ANDREWS

What is the programme of your dreams?

HATTIE

I think it's called *The Lady, the Troubadour, the Priest.*

ARIEL ANDREWS

Is it autobiographical?

HATTIE laughs.

ARIEL ANDREWS

And Joel, how about you?

JOEL

I'm still supposed to be starting rabbinical college in Gateshead in October, and somehow I have to find a way to let my parents know that's not what I intend to do any more.

ARIEL ANDREWS

So what are you going to do?

JOEL

I don't know yet. I have to get over this hurdle first.

ARIEL ANDREWS

Maybe consider the Jungian training? You'd make a good therapist. Could be a better way of being a rabbi?

JOEL

Ah. Ah. *(He is intrigued.)* Thank you; thank you for that. I'll work on it as an idea when I'm clear of this stuff.

ARIEL ANDREWS

Maybe it will help you get clear of the stuff. Look, here's a card from an old friend of mine who's been in practice for many years. She's good. She was analysed by Jung.

She takes a card from her notice board—the one tidy area in the room—and hands it to him. Joel takes it, looks at it. He is pleased.

ARIEL ANDREWS
OK, I have to go, my taxi will be here. Stay as long as you like.

She starts to tidy up in a desultory fashion.

HATTIE
Don't worry about the glasses, we'll wash them up.

CHARLIE
And we'll take the bottle out. Have a great time.

As the lecturer goes out of the door, she turns, looks at them for a moment:

ARIEL ANDREWS
You're the best three students I've ever had, you know. Thanks.

She sweeps out before they can reply.

They look at each other: camera tight in on their faces

CHARLIE
I think we just graduated.

Joel: filmscript 12

Rosa Lenkowitz

INT. ROSA LENKOWITZ' TREATMENT ROOM—EVENING

It is July 1971. JOEL and ROSA LENKOWITZ are sitting facing each other in comfortable chairs. It is a summer evening; some soft lighting. There is a small table in between them with a glass of water on it for JOEL. Flowers. Lots of books, comfortable spacious living room, not like an office. Earthy colours. She is Jewish. American. From New York City. Wealthy intellectual background. Elegant careful clothes, understated; modern silver jewellery. Dark cerise silk summer blouse. Room very warm and nurturing; so is she. But sharp mind.

Camera on JOEL's face.

JOEL
Is it true that you were analysed by Jung himself in Küsnacht?

ANALYST

Yes it is true; is that important to you?

JOEL

Here we go, always with the questions. You don't know my mother, do you?

ANALYST

(Laughs) I can see we're going to get on really well.

JOEL

That's important to you, is it?

Laughter.

INT. ROSA LENKOWITZ' TREATMENT ROOM—AFTERNOON

She is wearing different clothes. It is still July 1971. Different flowers in same vases. Otherwise, same room. JOEL still wears the yarmulke.

JOEL

I read that Jung once worked with a Jewish woman who had left the fold, and had a dream where he saw her as a Jewish saint. The outcome of the analysis was that she returned to her religion and her community.

ANALYST

Yes.

JOEL

OK, well, I want to go in the opposite direction. I'm definitely not a Jewish saint. It's not that I have no ambitions, but my ambition is to be an ex-saint. And that's why I want you to help me.

ANALYST

So tell me what you mean by the opposite direction.

JOEL

This is the way I feel. I don't have to find my roots—I have huge solid roots, that stretch back for millennia, but they don't feed me right. In fact they are starving me. In fact I'm going to drop this metaphor altogether. *(Pauses and looks down at his hands.)* What I am like is a little coloured helium balloon on a string, and there's a child holding that string. The child wants the balloon, but what the balloon wants is the sky, so much, so much, you can feel it tugging at that little grasping hand.

ANALYST
Who is this child?

Focus on JOEL's face—he is impassive.

INT. ROSA LENKOWITZ' TREATMENT ROOM—AFTERNOON

It is still July 1971. Same room, different clothes and flowers.

JOEL
My most pressing problem is, I'm due to start at rabbinical college in October, and I know I'm not going; and I just can't bring myself to tell my parents I'm not going. For a year now I've been living this double life: where I live, with my dear friends, I'm learning to be a gentile—with a few Jewish eccentricities and turns of phrase, you understand—but there's this whole other discourse going on: parents, extended family, friends of parents, friends of friends of parents… they are everywhere, and I allow them to see me as the Jewish saint: the future rabbi.

ANALYST
Yes.

JOEL
Externally I still keep a lot of the rules—it's easy enough to eat vegetarian, so that no-one notices that I'm actually keeping kashrut. I go to the synagogue Friday night and Saturday, and smile at the kind ladies who feed me and make plans for my future. And I'm useful to the men in the synagogue, because I can play an active part in the services: I've studied a lot. And they say, 'what a mitzvah, such a young man, doing what his parents want him to do'. Almost every other sentence they tell me how lucky my parents are.

Silence. The camera has analyst's point of view—watching JOEL's hands, gestures, body movements, etc.

JOEL
So this weekend I'm going to London on a visit home. This weekend I'm going to tell them. Help me.

Silence. He looks at camera—tears.

JOEL
Help me.

Silence.

INT. JOEL'S PARENTS' HOUSE: DINING ROOM—EVENING

It is July 1971. A very high-bourgeois North London home. Old paintings, solid furniture, sensible. An 8 branch candelabra. Books in Hebrew. A comfortably-off home where scholarly Judaism is much in evidence.

It's a bustling household—loads of people invited for Friday night meal, overwhelming bustle, Jewish conversation, aunts and uncles and children of all ages.

JOEL keeps trying to have THE conversation, but keeps getting interrupted by the following little vignettes—so he doesn't get the chance to speak at any time during the weekend.

These are really quick snatches. Repeatedly JOEL—in different locations in the house—is trying to speak with either his FATHER or his MOTHER, and each time he is interrupted by a loquacious relative or friend. Or child.

FEMALE RELATIVE 1

Joel, you are looking so well, (*turning to husband*) isn't he looking well my dear, (*turning to JOEL's mother*) he's looking so well.

FEMALE RELATIVE 2

Joel, when are you going to get your hair cut? (*Turning to JOEL's mother*) He's got such lovely hair, but it needs to be shorter than that.

FEMALE RELATIVE 3

(*To daughter*) he's taller than his uncle Moishe. Tall is good, tall is good, I like tall.

SMALL CHILD

(*Taking JOEL's hand*) Joel, Joel, come and see my new doll's house. Grandpa made it for me—come and see—come now.

FEMALE FAMILY FRIEND

Joel, meet my niece Miriam, she's clever like you, she's going to college.

She is holding the arm of a young girl—shy—she and JOEL are both extremely embarrassed.

FEMALE FAMILY FRIEND

I'll just leave you two to get to know each other.

Smiles and nods and leaves them. They just stare at each other.

INT. ROSA LENKOWITZ' TREATMENT ROOM—AFTERNOON

ANALYST

So, Joel, are you free now?

JOEL

I am so trapped; I am bound hand and foot. And Abraham is standing over me with a knife. What do I do? All weekend I tried to get my parents alone, all weekend I was surrounded—wall-to-wall relatives, being nice to me. Nice nice nice. Being nice to this nice Joel that is their nice creation.

ANALYST

So who are you, then, if not that person?

JOEL

Good question. I can't remember.

ANALYST

Joel, tell me a dream. Right now. The first that comes to your mind. Now.

Camera on his face.

Shock of realisation comes over his face; he recalls a really important dream that he had forgotten about.

JOEL

The dream. Oh, the dream!

DREAM SEQUENCE

INT. CASTLE: BEATRITZ' MUSIC ROOM—AFTERNOON

The room is much as before—it's early autumn. There are instruments and papers strewn around the room. It's BEATRITZ' music room.

BEATRITZ

The Inquisition is getting nearer; you know that, don't you? We heard today that there were burnings in Béziers. That is not far away.

PARFAIT

Yes, I heard. Many friends died there.

BEATRITZ

That is terrible—how can you bear it?

PARFAIT

I can bear it.

BEATRITZ

Why are you so calm? They will kill you, and all of your friends. They will burn you alive.

PARFAIT

Yes. I expect so. It says in their book 'I the Lord thy God am a jealous God'. It is not surprising that the servants of a jealous God behave in this fashion, is it?

BEATRITZ

Do you hate God?

PARFAIT

I hate nobody. I love God, and yearn towards him in my deepest heart every moment of my life. A loving God, a being of absolute purity; not a jealous God.

BEATRITZ

Where is this God of yours?

PARFAIT

He is here, Lady—where else would he be?

BEATRITZ

Do you not believe in the Bible?

PARFAIT

I do not believe in, or have anything to do with, the old Bible—the Bible of the jealous God.

BEATRITZ

What do you believe, then?

PARFAIT

Lady, I follow the Angel known as Jesus who was killed on the cross. I have received the transmission that he came to pass on to us. Because I have received it, I can give it to others. The transmission gives peace. You say I am calm, in the middle of hell; yes this is true. I am at peace. Of course, the test is the fire; but I have no doubts about that. I am content.

BEATRITZ

I can see that. I can hardly believe it, but I can see it. What must I give to have that peace?

PARFAIT

As the Angel said—everything, Lady, absolutely everything.

BEATRITZ

I cannot give you everything, I must be free. I must write my music. I must live my life and follow it where it goes.

PARFAIT

Yes, you must. We all must go through the fire in our own way. We must go through the fire to the light.

END DREAM SEQUENCE

INT. ROSA LENKOWITZ' TREATMENT ROOM—CONTINUOUS

Camera on JOEL's face, tears streaming down.

JOEL

Through the fire to the light.

INT. CHARLIE'S HOUSE: KITCHEN—LATER

JOEL comes in through the door to the kitchen. He goes straight to the phone to call his father. He's acting before he has a chance to change his mind.

JOEL

Oh hello, is Mr Cohen in please? Yes it is quite important, it's his son Joel, I need to speak to him. Thanks. Oh hi, it's Joel. Yes I'm fine—but I need to come down and have a serious talk with you. And it needs to be soon.

Pause

JOEL

No, no, I'm absolutely fine, I'm not in any trouble, but we need to speak. It needs to be somewhere where we can have a real conversation without being interrupted.

Pause

JOEL

OK, fine, yes—see you in your office tomorrow, 11.30.

Pause

JOEL

No, I won't need lunch. No, really, I won't need lunch, an hour should be fine, then I'll come straight back here.

Pause

JOEL

Yes, I love you too.

INT. MR COHEN'S OFFICE—MORNING

A study more than an office. Books covering walls. Heavy wood table, lots of books out. MR COHEN, *late fifties, grey hair, dark suit with waistcoat, black capel, small neat beard, silvery hair, glasses. Lined face. Looks kind.*

JOEL *has told him that he wants to stop being a Jew.*

MR COHEN *is in distress. Tears—head in hands, finds it hard to speak at first.*

JOEL

(Also in tears—speaking quietly) What can I do? The truth is the truth. You taught me that. I would rather be an honourable outcast than live as your son without truth.

MR COHEN

You are throwing away the most precious thing you have.

JOEL

I'm not throwing anything away. I would rather do almost anything than hurt you, but I will not pretend to a faith I don't have.

MR COHEN

A *faith,* you call it? How can you say that—you, my son? Have you forgotten what we are? We are *chosen.* We do not have choices. What we have is: duty. To our fathers. You have a duty to me. You have a duty to my father. To his ashes, in a chimney over Poland. How can you break faith with that?

JOEL

I'm going to do this. I understand you can't give me your blessing, but do we have to make it this painful?

MR COHEN

(Shouts—very angry) DON'T SPEAK TO ME ABOUT PAIN! If you do this thing, you will not see me, or your mother, again. You must choose.

Tight close-up on MR COHEN'S *face—he is a kind, intelligent, and civilised man who has completely lost control.*

MR COHEN (CONT.)

What the Nazis did to my father you have done to me. You have burned me up. If you are not a Jew you are not my son. YOU HAVE BURNED ME UP.

INT. CHARLIE'S HOUSE. MUSIC ROOM—EVENING

*Early evening in high summer—*CHARLIE *and* HATTIE *on sofa. She is reading.*

CHARLIE

He hasn't eaten for four days.

HATTIE

Let him be.

CHARLIE

We have to do something.

HATTIE

Let him be—he knows we're here; he has to do this by himself.

INT. CHARLIE'S HOUSE: JOEL'S ROOM—MORNING

JOEL *is asleep in a chair. He is unkempt. Hasn't shaved for four days—still wearing same clothes as he wore in his father's office—crumpled now. Still wearing the yarmulke. He is dreaming, and clearly troubled.*

DREAM SEQUENCE

EXT. CASTLE COURTYARD—MORNING

JOEL's *dream. It is a burning. Somewhat confused and hectic and unclear. A song arises out of the flames—a strong and simple melodic line. A female voice, singing in Provençal.*

Camera shots leave us confused as to who is being burned in the dream.

We see the PARFAIT *(who is* JOEL*), who may be being burned, or may be witnessing the burning. He is calm. There is a sense that the song sustains him, but we don't see who is singing it.*

END DREAM SEQUENCE

CUT TO:

INT. CHARLIE'S HOUSE: JOEL'S ROOM—MORNING

JOEL *wakes from the dream, gets up and leaves room—he is in a hurry.*

INT. CHARLIE'S HOUSE: STAIRCASE—CONTINUOUS

JOEL *running down several flights of stairs.*

INT. CHARLIE'S HOUSE: MUSIC ROOM—CONTINUOUS

HATTIE *and* CHARLIE *are still on sofa—both now reading in the music room.* JOEL *goes straight to piano and plays the song, 'Through the Fire to the Light', that he heard in the dream. He is emotional and intense but lit up and through the worst.*

> so, sister, here I stand
> we walk together—take my hand
> hold true to what we understand
> and sing to those who fear the flames
> of freedom
> fear and doubt we leave behind us
> let those who wait remind us
> we sing as those who know the flames
> of freedom
>
> through the fire—through the fire
> where heart and soul unite
> through the fire—through the fire
> to the light
>
> so, brother, here I stand
> we walk together—take my hand
> hold true to what we understand
> and sing to those who fear the flames
> of freedom
> fear and doubt we leave behind us
> let those who wait remind us
> we sing as those who know the flames
> of freedom
>
> through the fire—through the fire
> where heart and soul unite
> through the fire—through the fire
> to the light
>
> so, comrade, here I stand
> we walk together—take my hand
> hold true to what we understand
> and sing to those who fear the flames
> of freedom
> fear and doubt we leave behind us
> let those who wait remind us
> we sing as those who know the flames

of freedom

through the fire—through the fire
where heart and soul unite
through the fire—through the fire
to the light

INT. CONCERT HALL: SMALL—EVENING

The band (still just the three of them) are playing the song from the dream.
JOEL is not wearing his yarmulke.

Charlie: filmscript 13

Death and marriage

INT. CHARLIE'S HOUSE: KITCHEN—MORNING

It is the morning after JOEL's second 'through the fire' dream; he has seen
his father, had four bad days, dreamed, written the song. August 1971.

JOEL

(Holding a letter) They are not taking it. Even after those terrible things
that my father said to me; they are just refusing to believe it. My mother's taken over and unreality has been restored. What am I going to do
to make them see? It has to be a one-way trip. And I can't think of anything that's a one way trip. They will always have you back, they will
never stop asking.

CHARLIE

You could train for the Roman Catholic priesthood.

JOEL

Don't think it hasn't been tried; but you know my mother, she'd be on
the phone to the Pope, straight away.

Laughter

HATTIE

You must marry out.

JOEL

Yes, that would definitely do it—like nothing else *(it's clear he thinks this*
is a joke). Problem, Hattie—I have no-one to marry.

HATTIE
Sure you do. Me.

JOEL AND CHARLIE
You?

HATTIE
Why not?

JOEL
Because you don't believe in marriage.

HATTIE
That, dear, is the point. The whole point.

JOEL
(To CHARLIE) Are you OK about this?

CHARLIE
(To HATTIE) Where does that leave me?

HATTIE
Exactly where you are now. No more, no less. Marriage is nothing. This is an act of loving friendship. What's more, we can offer you two parts in the show. You get to be the best man, and you get to give the bride away. But you have to wear your clown suit. Deal?

CHARLIE
What about your parents?

HATTIE
Don't be ridiculous, it's nothing to do with them. And they are Communists, my love, they don't have too much invested in this bourgeois shit, you know.

CHARLIE
(To JOEL) Are you sure that this will do it?

JOEL
Oh yes. If I marry out I die. They sit shivah on me, exactly as if I had literally died.

CHARLIE
Really?

JOEL
Yes, really.

HATTIE

Look, trust me—this is the way forward. Just do it.

INT. REGISTRY OFFICE—MORNING

Camera on registrar—serious, droning. Camera pans round.

Almost empty office, little old lady (MILDRED) sits there smiling (a witness picked up in street).

Camera pans round.

HATTIE is wearing outrageously hippie caftan, and looks distinctly pregnant. JOEL in his best suit, which is now looking somewhat battered. No hat. Keeps nervously patting his head.

Pan round: starting at feet, reveal CHARLIE in clown suit.

HATTIE starts to make going-into-labour groaning noises. REGISTRAR nervously takes ceremony much faster. Ceremony concludes.

HATTIE

(To MILDRED) Thank you for being our other witness—I hope we didn't take too much of your time.

MILDRED

(Benign and a little bemused) Oh not at all, duck. I've had a smashing time.

CHARLIE and HATTIE link their arms in hers, help her out of her seat.

EXT. REGISTRY OFFICE: OUTSIDE—MORNING

The wedding group come out of the building into the sunshine on the street. CHARLIE and HATTIE still have their arms linked with MILDRED. They strew a bag of confetti all over her.

QUICK-FIRE STILLS

Snapshots of all four of them in different combinations—laughing and pulling funny faces. MILDRED is very much included in the playfulness—she's having a nice time—not taking things seriously.

HATTIE

(Patting her rounded belly) What's your name? We'd like to name this after you.

MILDRED

Ooh really? My name's Mildred.

HATTIE *whips out a teddy bear with a flourish from under her caftan and gives it ceremoniously to* MILDRED—*who laughs and laughs.*

HATTIE
Mildred, meet Mildred.

HATTIE *and* JOEL *and* CHARLIE *run off down Broad Street, laughing. They wave to* MILDRED—*she waves back. Close up of* MILDRED *holding teddy bear and smiling.*

Charlie: filmscript 14

Charlie's Grandfather

EXT. CHARLIE'S GRANDFATHER'S GARDEN—AFTERNOON

Garden of stately home. May 1971. Beautiful landscaped park. Tea on terrace; elderly man in wheelchair, upright military bearing. CHARLIE *and he are taking tea together.*

GRANDFATHER
How old are you now, Charles?

CHARLIE
I'll be 22 just after graduation.

GRANDFATHER
Oh yes, your famous redbrick education. Has it been a complete waste of time?

CHARLIE
Just as you predicted, it's led me into bad ways.

GRANDFATHER
Thank Christ for that—so you have learned something?

CHARLIE
I have two friends for life.

GRANDFATHER
Splendid, that's what you need. When I was your age I had no bits of paper, but I had friends I could trust with my life.

CHARLIE
What exactly were you doing when you were my age? Was that before you went into business with Uncle John?

GRANDFATHER

In the summer when I was 22, I was in France. It was 1917. I was a Captain in the 36th Ulster Regiment. In this month, in 1917, I was getting ready to lead men into the battle. We were going to take Messines Ridge. We did, too, damn it to hell; we did. I led them knowing full well that I would be leading many of them to death. They knew it too. And: we loved each other. There was never such love as that. Never. Did you know that? Is that in the books? Of course we didn't mention it, but everyone knew it.

CHARLIE

No, it's not in the books. Do you want it to be? I could write it for you, if you told me the story.

GRANDFATHER

Good God no—books can't do it. If you weren't there you have no right to know about it; that love, that death.

CHARLIE

Why are you telling me, then?

GRANDFATHER

Because I recognise something. There's something in you, young man—some steel. I've been sizing up men all of my life, and I can see something in you that I trust. Christ knows what it is, you've had this soft life, and what are you, some kind of an actor? You know damn all about life and less than nothing about death. But I know I could put you in charge of a platoon, and the men would follow you. You've got it, whatever it is. And that, dear boy, is why I called you here. I am going to give you an interesting gift. I'm shifting my money around at the moment—the accountants want me to loosen it up. I'm going to give rather a lot of it to you.

CHARLIE

Why?

GRANDFATHER

Because you will need it.

CHARLIE

Why?

GRANDFATHER

Well, the way the world is, if you're going to stay true to your potential, you are going to need a sizeable amount of go-to-hell money. I think what you will do is what you have in you, and my judgement—which is pretty damn good—tells me that it's important. Too important to waste any of it in making money. You need never think about money again. Any questions, see the accountants, but don't let them give you any advice. It's all taken care of.

CHARLIE

All right. But on one condition.

GRANDFATHER

Dear God—I'm about to give you a vast amount of money with no strings attached—and you have a condition! A condition! *(He laughs till he is helpless with laughter).* I haven't laughed like that for years—what incredible cheek. I knew you were made of the right stuff. What's your condition, boy?

CHARLIE

I have two friends—I love them as my life—I will share the money with them.

GRANDFATHER

Charles—it's your money—I'm backing you and your ability to make decisions.

CHARLIE

What can I say?

GRANDFATHER

Don't say anything—pour the tea. When you find the love that can go through fire, stick to it. Stick to it all your life. No milk, no sugar—doctor's orders.

Hattie: email

With panache

Hello dear Charlie,

Thank you so much for the pieces. I love them. I'd forgotten how funny the registry office affair was. You've captured it perfectly. Joel and I are really happy with the way your scenes are going. Truly. I'll cross them off the big list on the kitchen notice board. Actually, I'll get Charly to do it. She can do it with panache—and then I'll get to tell her what panache means and she can play with that too. I swear she gets more enchanting every day. But I don't need to tell you that.

So, without further ado and with no trumpets whatsoever, here are

1. A tiny piece from Joel with his parents sitting shivah—it needs to come right after your wedding scene I think. It's poignant. What a shame. So much unnecessary suffering.

2. A charming little sequence, also Joel's, that he never told us about at the time and which will be so sweet, and heart-warming, coming just next.

3. A conversation, from me, that I had with your marvellous mother a few days later. What happened to that painting, by the way?

I feel quite confident about this piece with your mother. I'm working on a more intricate, and intimate, piece that brings some of the twelfth century material together with our lives in that long, idyllic summer after Finals. I'm feeling less confident about how to do it—how to do it justice. It needs to be utterly truthful and not at all sentimental. I'm quite frightened by the intensity of memory it calls up, and find myself putting it off. But I'll give it proper care and attention this weekend, and get something to you by Sunday night. I'm happy to write the twelfth century material if that suits you best. Joel can help if I get stuck. You're absolutely right not to go on with the academic research though—tempting though it is, so much of it is simply conjecture, and we know the experiences we had speak the truth well enough, even if some of the details are at odds with the history books. What is history after all? Ah! I hear an Ariel Andrews lecture arising here—should we try and incorporate that lecture she did on the Provençal poets, do you think? Remember how it startled us at the time—so in tune with what we were experiencing. Alchemical. I'll write and ask her if she still has that lecture anywhere. Maybe she wrote it up as an article or something. I think she was translating some Troubadour poems at the time. Do you think she'd mind?

Do take good care of yourself, my beloved friend. I'm worried that you are feeling this even more intensely than I am. I imagine that's what all that academic research was about—classic displacement activity? I have little Charly and Murray and Kes and the daily joy of caring for the animals to keep me on the ground here. Hammersmith is great for theatres and cinemas and man-about-town frivolities, but doesn't really nourish the heart and soul. Do come and stay again when you can.

Little Charly is so excited about the costume. She rushes home from school each day to see if it's arrived yet. She thinks that you each need to perfect both the front and back ends. Says quite categorically that it's unprofessional (her word—honest!) to be over-specialised.

We send more love than you can imagine.

Hattie.

PS when next you write to little C, please can you use the word 'panache' a few times?

Joel: filmscript 15

Sitting Shivah

INT. JOEL'S PARENTS' HOUSE: LIVING ROOM—EVENING

September 1971. Parents dressed in black, sitting in a line at one end of the room on hard chairs. They are sitting shivah for their 'dead' son. Many friends and relatives come and go—they all bring food and leave it on the table The parents are in deep distress. There is a low hubbub of talk, from which you hear the occasional bubble-up of phrases like these: 'he was such a lovely boy', 'I'm so sorry he's gone', 'what a terrible thing' etc.

Joel: filmscript 16

The quest

MONTAGE: IMAGES OF JOEL

October 1971

These need to be described in detail

—Arrives at station, goes into forecourt.

—Going down to platform. Getting on to a train.

—Staring out of train window (suspense building, important trip).

—Getting off at Leeds station.

—Catches bus, looking around furtively.

—Joel across street from delicatessen—waiting for customers to clear.

INT. LEEDS DELICATESSEN—MORNING

Jewish delicatessen counter with dishes piled high with good traditional food. Elderly, kindly Jewish man with capel and white coat behind counter—recognises JOEL *as he enters shop. No other customers.*

SHOPKEEPER

Sorry to hear about your death.

JOEL

Yes, it was very painful.

SHOPKEEPER

How are you feeling now?

JOEL

Couldn't be better. I could equally well say, 'couldn't be worse', but then people would be upset.

Laughter—there is a tough minded sympathy between them; almost tender—but not sentimental.

SHOPKEEPER

What you need is some of my chopped herring.

JOEL

Why do you think I came all the way from Birmingham? Can I have it intravenously?

SHOPKEEPER

What would be the point of that? You'd miss the pleasure.

Speeded up scene, where he makes up a huge package of stuff; chopped herring, gherkins, smoked salmon, bagels etc—two bags' worth.

JOEL *offers to pay him.*

SHOPKEEPER

No, it's a wedding present.

JOEL

I couldn't possibly.

SHOPKEEPER

Please—accept. And be sure to give my best respects to your wife.

JOEL

Thank you. Thank you. *(They are both moved by this.)*

Hattie: filmscript 17

Olivia

INT. OLIVIA'S STUDIO—MORNING

September 1971. Big messy bright room—attic skylights—a kitchen area—big sink—old chairs—a big table etc. HATTIE is having her portrait painted by CHARLIE's mother. She is posing.

OLIVIA

For a member of the proletariat, you are delightfully eccentric.

HATTIE

Never underestimate the class enemy, my dear.

Laughter. OLIVIA's laugh is like HATTIE's. They are very comfortable together.

HATTIE

So what is it you don't like about the women's movement?

OLIVIA

Earnest, strident, ungainly, humourless. And no room to dance.

HATTIE

Do you know that Emma Goldman quote?

OLIVIA

Red Emma?

HATTIE

Yes—'If I can't dance I don't want to be in your revolution'.

OLIVIA

(Laughs) Exactly. Time for a break.

She lights another cigarette. Puts kettle on. Makes coffee: plunger method. Scene is chaos. Paint stains. Canvases. They sit together on an old lumpy sofa.

OLIVIA

So how is my son?

HATTIE

He's about to be an RSC actor. Third sailor in *The Tempest*—Garamond directing.

OLIVIA
Bloody hell, I knew him when he was a first year art student. Pretentious bastard, he was. Impressed everybody under the sun, though. He was very good at that.

HATTIE
Charlie is not impressed.

OLIVIA
No, I wouldn't have thought so. It will end in tears, I expect.

HATTIE
That's show business.

OLIVIA
Are you in love with Charlie?

HATTIE
I love him very much; there's a difference.

OLIVIA
Do people get married at all nowadays?

HATTIE
I got married three days ago, as a matter of fact.

OLIVIA
Oh, anyone I know?

HATTIE
Yes, Joel.

OLIVIA
The Rabbi?

HATTIE
Not any more.

OLIVIA
(Laughs) How does Charlie feel about this?

HATTIE
He gave away the bride—and he was the best man. In a clown suit.

OLIVIA
Ah. And, if I may dare to ask, how does the relationship between the three of you stand currently?

HATTIE

Just where it always did, and always will: we love each other.

OLIVIA

You really are eccentric, aren't you?

HATTIE

My Dad always taught me—never let anyone put you in a category.

OLIVIA

You're beginning to talk like the aristocracy. *(Laughs)* I would like to meet your father.

HATTIE

You would have a great deal to say to each other—not all of it complimentary.

OLIVIA

My father always taught me: decide what you are going to do, and do it. He hated me going to art college—all those pacifist young men. He fought me all the way, but he loved me for fighting back—and winning.

HATTIE

Charlie is going to get into a fight over the *Tempest* production, you know.

OLIVIA

Yes. Garamond is a waste of time. And my son Charlie is not a time waster. And neither am I: get back in that chair before the light moves too much.

Charlie: letter

Panache

My dear Charly

Your mother, whom as you know I adore, has asked me to write to you about panache. My life's study, my middle name, my daily devoir. So I will happily do this. But, there is a problem: how will you, precious friend, ask questions and interrupt the flow in the necessarily monolinear medium of a letter? Aha! I will ask the questions for you! Like this…

Imagine a small beautiful child, soft midnight eyes, skin the colour of cappuccino, inexplicably clad in a rabbit suit, sitting adoringly at the feet of a strikingly handsome individual wearing a deerstalker hat and smoking an impressively large meerschaum pipe. He speaks:

—Panache, properly considered, exists at many different levels.

—Stop smoking that horrible pipe, Charlie.

—But—

—*Chaar*lie!

He puts out the pipe, in a dignified manner, and continues:

—Many different levels. At one level—

—Your middle name is Peregrine.

—Be silent, child, that's classified information. Now. At the most obvious level, panache is the ability to walk up walls.

—Like in the movie?

—Exactly. The immortal Cosmo, panache personified. And when they expect you to walk up walls, don't; fall through them, instead. And: make them laugh.

—So I should learn to walk up walls! Cool!

—No! No! That's something that only *old* people do. You my dear already have wonderful panache. Wonderful.

—Do I? How?

—Listen, for a minute, and learn. Panache is purified pride. Panache is poetry. Panache is—

—Pink petunias?

—Exactly! By George, I think you've got it! It is—well, you know how everyone you meet more or less does what you expect them to do, only not?

—Yes.

—Well, the 'not' is panache. Everyone has it, no-one is totally predictable, even the Following Cat sometimes doesn't follow you.

—The Following Cat is much more like a pink petunia than you will ever be, Charlie.

—*Touché, chère lapinette.* Anyway, most people like the predictable so they try and predict you and predict you until you turn into a pudding.

—I like pudding.

—Not *boring* pudding, surely? Of course not. Anyway, the thing to do, is not. Is to stop them. Is not to be where they expect you to be. And: make them laugh. Make them see the world anew, fresh, born yesterday, bright as a button, make them rock and roll, make them love you nervously, make them live, Charly my darling, make them live. That, that is panache.

Charly: email

Panache

Here for you Charlie is two pink petunias (in a photo I took ages ago because they were so pink) (in Henley in a hanging basket) because you are the perfect prince of panache, in fact you are the principal pellucid panjandrum, and I love you.

xx

Hattie: email

Intro: big sky mind

Dearest—here you are. I stayed up all night to finish it. In the end it was more about editing it down than finding more things to say. I'm happy with it. Joel's happy with it. But it's really really important to us that you should be entirely at ease with it. If there's anything at all that you want to be said or shown differently, then please just say. This is all our lives.

Our love to you—don't leave it too long this time. I'm anxious about this.

Hattie.

PS We're going to Dad's for a non-Christmas Christmas. I know it's a busy season for clowns, but you're more than welcome to join us if you care to. Or, if you need some semi rural peace and quiet, Murray will be here taking care of the animals and in semi-retreat himself. Just say the word, beloved. Please just say.

Hattie: filmscript 18

Big sky mind

EXT. CASTLE GARDEN—MORNING

*A few days have passed since the initial meeting of Beatritz and the Trou-
badour.*

BEATRITZ
I've asked the skylark. Do you want to hear my song?

TROUBADOUR
Is it the skylark's song?

BEATRITZ
Of course.

She starts to sing:

> can vei la lauzeta mover
> de joi sas alas contral rai
> que so'oblida'e.s laissa chazer
> per la soussor c'al cor li vai

> when I see the skylark move
> with joy his wings against the sun
> and so forget himself that, falling,
> he dies into his own delight

TROUBADOUR
Picks up accompaniment, adds a verse

> anc non agui de mon poder
> ni no fui meus de l'or'en sai
> que.m laisser en sos olhs vezer
> en un miralh que mout me plai

> I have no sense of being me
> nor am I ruler of myself
> since in her eyes she let me see
> my self. This mirror is delight.

They sing the last verse together

> miralhs, pus me merie en te,
> m'an mort li sospir de preon,

104

c'aissi.m perdei com perdet se
lo bels narcuisus en la fon

mirror I mirror me in you
and breathe myself away, and die;
losing me as he was lost
Narcissus in the river's echo

Visually we are swimming round landscape. It blurs into green, and we go up like the skylark. Skylark point of view on these two characters, then the bird flies over fields and fields, to overview next scene.

EXT. A FIELD—AFTERNOON

The bird swoops above HATTIE *and* CHARLIE, *singing the same song with guitar accompaniment, in a field in the English countryside—July flowers. Summer 1971.*

Camera comes down to regular level.

They make love—wordless and beautiful. Romantic soft focus.

The song takes us back to the twelfth century: a blurred transition.

EXT. CASTLE GARDEN—MORNING

Continuation of previous TROUBADOUR/LADY *scene*

TROUBADOUR

So it is true, then, what they say about you and your songs.

BEATRITZ

True enough. Though what they say about me and my songs is usually motivated by the desire for a free lunch.

TROUBADOUR

Lady, when I heard your music my soul left my body *(he is not being ironic here).*

BEATRITZ

Yes, I could hear that in your lute: the lute is not interested in a free lunch.

EXT. A FIELD—AFTERNOON

Continuation of lovemaking scene.

HATTIE

(Holding a guitar, laughing)

No strings attached!

She is lying in long grass and flowers—happy, light-hearted and free. She is contained and separate as always. We don't see CHARLIE's *reaction to this.*

EXT. CASTLE GARDEN—MORNING

Continuation of previous scene.

BEATRITZ

This lover of yours, whose name you cannot mention, is it she who inspires your songs?

TROUBADOUR

In a manner of speaking.

BEATRITZ

Speak more plainly.

TROUBADOUR

Some things are rather complicated.

BEATRITZ

I do not care for complication. Our spirits have met in the music. Tell me the truth. All my life people have fed me with metaphors, compliments, courtesies, meretricious nonsense. I think you can tell me the truth. Do so.

TROUBADOUR

Lady, you cut me to the heart. Here is the truth of my heart. There is a feeling, a longing, an enormous desire, like a bow pulled back, an incredible tension, that can send an arrow into the sky. Most men follow that desire slavishly, and seek to satisfy it as soon as they can, like animals. What we do is to ride the passion, not satisfy it, so that it can send an arrow into the sky. The arrow is our music. The sky is ... the sky.

BEATRITZ

(Seeking clarity and practicality) So this Lady is imaginary?

TROUBADOUR

If we are blessed, then we find a woman who can be this desire, who can call up in us the anguish and power of love. Who can be for us the Lover, the focus of passion, the sky.

All of this is intercut with flashes of HATTIE *and* CHARLIE *in the field, making love.*

HATTIE knows this truth, and CHARLIE doesn't yet.

BEATRITZ

So that is the truth of your art; what is the truth of your life?

TROUBADOUR

Lady, you cut deeper yet. I think they are the same thing.

BEATRITZ

Haven't you thought about it before?

TROUBADOUR

Lady, I had not met you. I had not truly met desire.

EXT. A FIELD—AFTERNOON

Continuation of lovemaking scene.

HATTIE is picking a bunch of flowers which will appear in scene with JOEL below.

CHARLIE

Yeats says, the intellect of man is forced to choose: perfection of the life or of the art.

HATTIE

(Laughs and laughs, louder and louder)

Such bullshit. Such incredible bullshit!

CHARLIE is hurt. Then he joins in the laughter—gradually at first. He is endearing here.

INT. CASTLE: BEATRITZ' MUSIC ROOM—EVENING

Candlelight. We have a sense of BEATRITZ having been taught by the PAR-FAIT over a period of time.

BEATRITZ

I have asked the skylark and all I hear is music. So, I ask you again: if this is hell, how do we get out of it?

PARFAIT

Where did the music of the skylark take you?

BEATRITZ

Deep inside myself, into my own music.

PARFAIT

That is where the answer lies.

BEATRITZ

My friend the Troubadour tells me that the answer lies in love.

PARFAIT

Yes, Lady, I would say that too.

BEATRITZ

But you are celibate, are you not?

PARFAIT

Lady, I think you will find that so is he.

BEATRITZ

Are you saying that men and women should not unite in love?

PARFAIT

I am only saying that men and women should not unite in desire. Anything you cling to will keep you in prison.

BEATRITZ

I love my music; should I let it go?

PARFAIT

The question is, does it take you to a place of unity, or a place of separation?

BEATRITZ

It takes me inside myself.

PARFAIT

And when you go there, who do you find?

BEATRITZ

As she speaks, she goes from intelligent/quizzical to utter peace.

When the music is most true, there is no-one to find. I—who am not I—am everything and nothing.

INT. CHARLIE'S HOUSE: MUSIC ROOM—AFTERNOON

On table are the flowers that HATTIE picked in the field—still fresh: home in on them to show the scene with CHARLIE has just happened. JOEL and HATTIE—intense.

JOEL

I've heard it said that when you know you are everything, that's compassion, and when you know you are nothing, that's wisdom; and life is a dance between these two.

HATTIE
As long as there's dancing involved, I'm in favour.

JOEL laughs.

HATTIE
There's got to be a song in there somewhere.

HATTIE is messing around on the guitar, starts to sing 'Big Sky Mind'. They compose the song together, toing and froing. In a way, they are making love.

> big sky mind—big sky mind
> that's all I'm asking
> all I'm asking you for, baby
> big sky mind—big sky mind
> that's all or nothing
> that I'm asking for
>
> let me fly to the sun through the filters of time
> where the intimate hum of the universe plays
> let me fly through the haze of the meaningless phrase
> to the peace of your big sky mind
>
> big sky mind—big sky mind
> that's all I'm asking
> all I'm asking you for, baby
> big sky mind—big sky mind
> that's all or nothing
> that I'm asking for
>
> let me fall through your eyes to the back of beyond
> where the intricate dance of the galaxies plays
> let me fall through the gaze of the ancients of days
> to the peace of your big sky mind
>
> big sky mind—big sky mind
> that's all I'm asking
> all I'm asking you for, baby
> big sky mind—big sky mind
> that's all or nothing
> that I'm asking for

let me float as the warmth of the dappledawn morning
let me skim like a stone from the ocean to shore
let me find myself lost on the new day's horizon
in the peace of your big sky mind

big sky mind—big sky mind
that's all I'm asking
all I'm asking you for, baby
big sky mind—big sky mind
that's all or nothing
that I'm asking for

HATTIE
Bliss!

JOEL
Exactly. I've also heard it said that bliss is the absence of desire.

HATTIE
Is that how it is for you?

JOEL
I'm not sure.

Camera focuses on the flowers—they are vibrant.

INT. CONCERT HALL: SMALL—EVENING

Small venue—just HATTIE, JOEL, CHARLIE—early days of band. They perform the song: 'Big Sky Mind'.

January 2004

Hattie, Charlie

Can you hear me?

Charlie—this is me, Hattie. Can you hear me? Can you give me any sort of sign? It's Tuesday. You're here with us. In the room above the music room—your old room. You've nothing to worry about. Hilary's phoned everyone—spoken to everyone personally. It's all sorted. Everything's on hold. And I'm sorting out any money complications, of course. We're a good team, Hilary and me. You just rest, my love. Rest and do whatever it is you need to do. We'll be here. I'll be here. I won't leave you, I promise.

Charly: blog

Sick with love

Mum came into my room, early. She never does that. Her serious face. She was pale and looked thin. We had this conversation:

—What's wrong, what's wrong?

—Charlie's here.

—Hey!

—He's sick.

—What's the matter with him?

—His mind is sick. He needs to rest. For now he is here and not here. His body is here but he has gone inside. When he is ready, when he has done the inside work, then he will come out again.

—Will he be the same, when he comes out?

111

—No. He will be better. Different, and better.

—When will he come out?

—I don't know.

—Are you absolutely sure he will come out?

She looked at me, as if she was making up her mind.

—I don't know, she said.

I felt sick with love. I knew you could feel this because of when Fritz the little kitten died, and we stayed with him, and when my Ayesha wouldn't come out, and times like that, sick, with love.

—Can I see him?

—Can you handle this? she said, quite sharply, as if I was grown up. Yes, I said. Yes yes. Go away now please and I will find out how to handle it and then I will be able to handle it.

So I lay on my bed and talked to Joel, didn't I, dear Joel, and you said, sleep for a little, my love, and so I went into dreamy sleep. And of course Rinpoche came. I heard him saying the words, the chanting words, and he gave me the permission. You have to have the permission, you see, from a high person, or the chanting words don't work properly, or not as well anyway, I don't know. But you must.

So I woke up then very clear with the words in my head, *om ah hung benza guru pema siddhi hung,* in Rinpoche's big deep inside voice, like a mouth organ inside, and I was fine and not sick. And went down and got some cornflakes because I would need the vitamins. And Mum looked at me, thin, she was sick with love, and I said, it will be fine, it will. So she took me up and Charlie was there in bed breathing, just breathing, oh all of his fire was out. So I sat and held his hand, oh his papery hand, and made myself very calm and kind, and said the chanting words, again and again, with a mouth organ inside me, and I could feel the room change. It changed, didn't it, Joel? Like turning on a light. Then I wasn't frightened any more, and after a while the heat came, inside me and through my hand to his paper hand, and I knew it would be OK. Whatever happened. Just like with little Fritz. Whatever happened, I knew it would be OK.

Charly, Charlie

Gone inside

Hello Charlie. I like it that you're here now all the time, even though I know you're not really here but gone away. Mum says you've gone inside to do the work, and then you'll come back. At least I think she said you'll come back. I would like that please Charlie.

I've got to go to school now but I'll see you later, when I come home. Won't I?

Hattie, Charlie

Please come home

Oh Charlie this is so hard. This is worse than Joel. Worse than Mum. Worse than the baby. Those were hard enough—but at least there was something to do. Nothing to be done—nothing. Nothing.

Please come back Charlie. Please come home.

Charly: blog

A ghost of Charlie

Charlie is a ghost of Charlie. When he moves, it is very slow. As if it hurts. He doesn't look at me, or at anyone. His me is not in. The room is full of flowers. They keep coming, the flowers, it is amazing. And children's drawings. Pictures of clowns, from dying children, wishing him well. Every day more and more. He is surrounded by colour, and he has no colour at all, his glow is not.

Joel, Hattie

I'm frightened he'll die

—Hattie—Hattie—you must get some rest.

—I'm frightened to leave him, Joel. I'm frightened he'll die if I'm not here by his bedside and awake.

—Yes I know. Leave me to watch over him.

—Oh Joel—I don't think you understand how I feel.

—I think perhaps I do. You know I don't feel the same about life and death as you do. I can't. But believe me, your staying awake is not the thing that's going to make the difference. Please go to sleep, darling. If only because Charly is worried seeing you like this.

—Joel Cohen—only you could pull the Jewish mother guilt trick at a time like this.

—There—you're laughing. That's better. Go to the kitchen and get some good food—eat—eat—then come back here and sleep beside him. Your energy will reach him just the same—better maybe.

—You'll wake me if he needs me?

—I promise.

—You'll be here all the time?

—I'm always here for you Hattie. You know that.

Charly, Charlie

A present

Hello Charlie, It's me again and the Following Cat. I'm going to give you your name back now because you need it all to yourself for a bit I think. Till you remember who you are. I would like that to be soon please Charlie but only if that's OK with you. No pressure. Thank you for lending me your name, Charlie. I'm still your darling. Your darling Rinchen.

Hattie, Charlie

Breakfast

Charlie—it's morning now. Can you hear me? I've brought you some breakfast. Can you smell it? Rinchen squeezed the oranges for you. Try to sip from this cup. I'll hold it steady. Please? Just a little. Oh God I sound like Joel. I've written a new scene. Would you like to hear it?

Rinchen, Hattie

Sing me a song

—Sing me a song, Mum.

—What sort of song?

—An everything's gonna be all right song.

—Rinchen—you know I always tell you the truth, don't you?

—Yes. Yes, I do.

—Rinchen—I can't truthfully sing you that sort of song right now.

—Why? Why?

—Because I don't know that everything's going to be all right.

—What do you know?

—I know that everything is just as it needs to be and that everyone's doing the best they can. I know that we love each other and understand each other: you—Charlie—Joel—me.

—And the Following Cat?

—Yes darling—and of course the Following Cat.

—Then sing the song.

February 2004

Hattie, Charlie

Tempest intro

Hello Charlie. Did you sleep much? You've had some breakfast today. I'm so pleased. And Murray's hair cut looks good. Rinchen is out riding. It's a beautiful morning—almost spring like, though it's only early February. There's some light blossom on some of the early cherry trees. Crocuses along the drive. Snowdrops everywhere. Would you like the window open now? The air smells so fresh today. Let me help you into the sunlight a little more. There. There you go. Easy does it.

Now, dear. Joel and I have written some more of the filmscript. Is it OK with you if I read it to you? I think it'll help, darling. I really do.

Well, I'll just start. If it gets too much just indicate—just a tiny gesture will do. Yes. Yes. A little movement. Have you got an 'It's OK to try, Hattie' signal for me today? Good. Good. Thank you, Charlie.

We decided to go for those *Tempest* scenes—the autumn after graduation. Joel's got such a good memory for details—especially the storm in a teacup thing. I think I was probably laughing too much at the time to take it all in. You'll love it, I know you will. Here goes.

Hattie, Joel: filmscript 19

Tempest

INT. CHARLIE'S HOUSE: KITCHEN—AFTERNOON

Early autumn 1971. JOEL and HATTIE are at the table talking. CHARLIE enters.

JOEL

What's wrong? You look awful. Have some cinnamon toast.

He passes a plate piled high with cinnamon toast that he and HATTIE *have been eating—flurry of activity around pouring tea.*

CHARLIE

Somehow I don't think cinnamon toast is going to do it. Actually, I want a drink.

Helps self to a large whisky from a bottle in a cupboard. JOEL *and* HATTIE *look at each other.* CHARLIE *is not a drinker.*

HATTIE

What is it? What's going on?

CHARLIE

The rehearsal was appalling. The interpretation is disgusting. The director is mad.

JOEL

That's not very unusual, is it?

CHARLIE

No, but this is. It is really really too much. Garamond is the hottest director in the world at the moment, and it's driven him mad: he has to keep being shockingly original, and so he's thought up a *Tempest* that is simply appalling. Caliban is the hero. He narrates the whole thing: he's like a narrative presence, on stage the whole time. The attempted rape of Miranda is a revolutionary political act. Prospero is the villain, the colonialist. Caliban's conspiracy with the sailors is Maoist guerrilla warfare.

JOEL

Ah, *The Tempest* by the Communist Party of Great Britain open brackets Marxist Leninist close brackets.

HATTIE

Sounds more like a first year essay to me: 'Shakespeare our Comrade'.

JOEL

Well, look on the bright side—you're playing third sailor in the tempest scene, with precisely one line, that no-one can hear anyway because the storm effects will be too loud. I don't think you're going to be compromising your artistic integrity. Look on it as an experience.

CHARLIE

The only problem will be if Max gets sick.

JOEL

Max? You mean Caliban?

CHARLIE

Right: it's a great honour, you see *(gestures to indicate irony).* They've chosen me to understudy him. This is a very big deal for someone straight out of University. My agent is ecstatic. I knew I should have taken the radio soap opera job.

HATTIE

She'd have been even more ecstatic.

CHARLIE

Yeah, right. The problem is, I can't bear it. I can just about stomach the way that man is lionised—everyone running around after him as if he were a God: he can say and do whatever he likes, and people just go on praising him. But what I can't take is him taking this exquisite, subtle, pain-filled play and turning it into sub-Marxist Punch and Judy show.

JOEL

Look—just sit through the rehearsals and figure out how it should be done. And don't throw up in public. It's only show business, after all.

CHARLIE responds by springing into a song and dance act. He starts with 'There's no business like show business', segues into 'Make them laugh' from Singin' in the Rain. *The others join in and the mood lifts.*

Several weeks later...

INT. CHARLIE'S HOUSE. MUSIC ROOM—AFTERNOON

JOEL is doodling on the piano, quietly. CHARLIE *is sitting staring into space. There is an atmosphere. Enter* HATTIE.

HATTIE

OK, what's going on?

JOEL

Caliban's broken a leg. Charlie has just got the understudy's dream come true. He's on tonight—press preview, RSC. God obviously loves him.

CHARLIE

Which God is that one, then?

HATTIE

What are you going to do?

CHARLIE

What can I do? Do the part, that's what. Do you realise I'm going to be on stage all the time? This bloody production doesn't even have an interval.

JOEL

I can see that he might not give a damn about the audience's collective bladder, but what about the loss in bar takings?

CHARLIE

As soon as this play is over they'll hit the bar like a breaking wave, in order to celebrate getting out. Meantime, however, I'm on the fucking stage during the whole show: I carry the entire weight of this ghastly production. Me. Caliban.

HATTIE

Charlie, you've got a job to do.

CHARLIE

My job is to follow direction.

HATTIE

Your job is to tell the truth.

CHARLIE

Hattie, this Garamond guy is possibly the most powerful person in British serious theatre at this moment. Everybody loves him. The establishment loves him, the anti-establishment loves him. It's only me that thinks he's a piss-artist.

HATTIE

Charlie, you've got a job to do.

CHARLIE

So you want me to tell Garamond that his entire conception of the play is wrong—on opening night, in front of the world's press, TV coverage inevitable? It'll be in all the newspapers tomorrow. This is what you want me to do?

HATTIE

Charlie, I want you to do Shakespeare. And, my dear, that's what you want too. What do you have to lose?

CHARLIE

I could be the laughing-stock of the entire theatrical business by midnight tonight, and, on top of that, my agent wouldn't love me any more.

HATTIE

Sounds good to me. It's about time you stopped taking this stuff so seriously.

CHARLIE goes into the following comic routine. It's mostly mime, but while miming, he's doing a narrative commentary and all of the voices. It's like Robin Williams—fast—manic—lots of voices—slightly hysterical.

CHARLIE leaps into the middle of room, makes a big gesture,

CHARLIE

Ladies and gentlemen, I give you, at the RSC, for one night only, the don't take it so seriously *(different voice)*—darling you must be joking—seriously career breaking *Tempest.*

Blare of trumpets. *(He does trumpet noise).*

CHARLIE

(As CALIBAN, urban guerrilla (Mexican accent))

As wicked dew as e'er my mother brush'd

With raven's feather from unwholesome fen

Drop on you both! a south-west blow on ye

And blister you all o'er!

He speaks and acts out the following reactions.

(As NARRATOR) Prospero is startled *(he moves to a Gielgud impersonation)* Dear boy don't you think you're being a little hysterical?

(As NARRATOR) Caliban strangles him. *(Mimes both the strangler and strangled)*

The audience starts to scream in horror.

(As AUDIENCE) Oh no, eek!

(As NARRATOR) The actors rush to overpower Caliban—who is out of control now; he pulls out a large knife.

(As CALIBAN) Fascist pigs, I'll slaughter the lot of you!

(As NARRATOR) Ariel throws a hissy fit.

(As ARIEL—very camp) He's dragging all our careers down with him!

(As NARRATOR) Miranda faints on top of Ariel; Ariel, not to be upstaged, faints on top of Miranda.

The Director comes on—he engages in a fist fight with Caliban, swapping Marxist-Leninist insults:

(As BOTH:) Capitalist running dog! Neo-Trotskyist revanchist anarcho-syndicalist revisionist motherfucker!

(As NARRATOR) Enter Shakespeare.

(As SHAKESPEARE—strong Birmingham accent) Excuse me, lads, but what the fuck are you playing at?

(As NARRATOR) The Director and Caliban both stop fighting for a moment and look at Shakespeare.

(As DIRECTOR) Thank God you're here, this man is destroying my play!

(As SHAKESPEARE) It's my fucking play, you big soft get, and you're the one who's destroying it.

(As NARRATOR) Shakespeare delivers a neat uppercut, knocks him out.

(As SHAKESPEARE) Come on, lad, let's go and get pissed. I like a good clown. Now, when Robert Armin did that part—

CHARLIE *turns to audience with final flourish:*

(BBC announcer voice) And that, ladies and gentlemen, is the don't take it too seriously storm in a teacup *Tempest.*

HATTIE *and* JOEL *are in hysterics, absolutely helpless with laughter. They applaud, feebly.*

CHARLIE
(After things have calmed down a bit) OK, supposing I do this, I shall be both very famous and very unemployable. What then?

HATTIE
It's not as if you need the money, is it? *(Gangster voice)* We'll have the getaway car at the stage door—as soon as you make your exit. Oh, and another thing—

CHARLIE
Yes?

HATTIE
Don't stop to pee.

CHARLIE

(Very luvvy) But darling, what about the curtain call?

They just look at him.

JOEL

You're going to play Caliban for laughs—and you want a curtain call?

CHARLIE

OK, no curtain call. *(Luvvy again)* But what about my career? *(More serious voice)* Hattie, what will I do?

HATTIE

Have you heard about Wavy Gravy?

HATTIE exits.

CHARLIE and JOEL look at each other—puzzled and amused.

CHARLIE

Wavy Gravy?

They shrug—in a good humoured way: they expect she'll explain at some point.

EXT. CAMPER VAN OUTSIDE RSC THEATRE—EVENING

The camper van is parked by stage door. Engine is running. It's the getaway car.

JOEL and HATTIE are playing the music from Bonnie and Clyde.

From the theatre they hear laughter and whoops and whistles—mayhem inside. They look at each other in awe and wonder.

JOEL

Er, I think he really did it...

EXT. CAMPER VAN OUTSIDE RSC THEATRE—CONTINUOUS

CHARLIE comes running out—still in CALIBAN costume. Engine is revving. It's raining.

EXT. CAMPER VAN OUTSIDE RSC THEATRE—CONTINUOUS

*HATTIE opens the front left door—*Bonnie and Clyde *music is playing. CHARLIE leaps in. He is slightly hysterical.*

CHARLIE

Where's the fucking sepia? If you haven't got sepia I'm not getting in.

JOEL

Where's your imagination? Call yourself an actor?

CHARLIE

Not any more, sunshine, not any more ever again.

EXT. CAMPER VAN OUTSIDE RSC THEATRE—CONTINUOUS

Van roars off into the night—Bonnie and Clyde *music plays jubilantly.*

NEXT MORNING

INT. CHARLIE'S HOUSE. MUSIC ROOM—MORNING

Sunday papers all over the place. Coffee cups. Remains of breakfast tray.
HATTIE *and* JOEL *and* CHARLIE *still in pyjamas and dressing gowns. Pop*
music on radio as background noise. CHARLIE *has hangover—groans—*
HATTIE *hands him alkaseltzer drink. It's only part way through this scene*
that you realise that there's been a mixed reaction to his radical theatre
act: that it is actually (partly) a wild success.

JOEL

Well, you really really did it, didn't you?

CHARLIE

I have here a telegram from the great man himself. Shall we say he was
more than a little disappointed? In fact, what he says is—I will never ever
work in any reputable theatre anywhere whatsoever in the English speaking world ever again so there. Stop.

Phone rings. HATTIE *goes out of the room to answer it.* JOEL *and* CHARLIE
carry on reading out reviews.

JOEL

Understudy goes mad and wrecks production.

CHARLIE

Storm about *Tempest:* understudy takes over.

JOEL

Classic production destroyed by unknown actor.

CHARLIE *groans—They read on in silence for a while—*HATTIE's *voice is*
heard faintly in background on phone—indistinct—she comes in and hears
the end of the following newspaper article.

JOEL

Hey, listen to this one: 'In one of the most remarkable scenes ever to happen in British theatre, an unknown understudy taking the part of Caliban at the last moment (due to an unfortunate accident to Max Lephroig) set out to deliberately sabotage Garamond's profound and imaginative interpretation of Shakespeare's last play. 'I am distraught and disgusted' said the director last night. 'I gave that boy his chance, and he turned and savaged me. I just can't understand why anyone would do a thing like that.'

Members of the audience, however, felt differently. 'It was hilarious' said one. 'I haven't laughed as much in the theatre since we went to that hand-bag play'. Another commented, 'When he started repeating Prospero's lines after him in funny voices I thought I would fall out of my seat. And then the tap-dancing was just amazing—so skilful. And the Fred Astaire imitation. How anyone could do Charlie Chaplin and Fred Astaire at the same time as that air is full of voices speech beats me. And wearing big boots and a beard too. This boy is a genius.'

HATTIE has come back into the room during this paragraph.

JOEL

'The actor in question, Charles Beaumont, was unavailable for comment last night . We understand that the production will open again next week with Jeffrey Philips playing Caliban strictly according the director's vision.'

HATTIE

Just for you, darling, I'm being a secretary. *(Pulls face)* Do you—or do you not—want to be on that arty farty review programme on BBC2 tonight? You are now rather famous, you see.

CHARLIE

Well, that's an interesting question.

JOEL

Do you want to be slow cooked or flash fried?

HATTIE

They're waiting—what shall I say?

CHARLIE shrugs: quizzical expression.

HATTIE

That's a 'no' then?

She leaves room to deliver message

THAT EVENING

INT. CHARLIE'S HOUSE. MUSIC ROOM—EVENING

The phone in the hall is ringing.

HATTIE

OK: half the world thinks you're a genius, and the other half think you ought to be locked up. I have now turned you down for sixteen interviews, two pantos, one lead role in *Waiting for Godot,* and the pilot for a TV sitcom. Oh, and there was a proposal of marriage. I turned that down too. All the rest were from your agent. She is quite upset. And I am now very sick of being a secretary: I quit.

She goes out to hall and brings in phone on long lead. gives it to JOEL, who answers it. JOEL listens intently, interesting expression on his face. The others are looking exhausted and drained.

JOEL

Hello. *(Pause)* Yes it is. *(Pause)* Yes I'm speaking for him. *(Pause)* Oh. *(Pause)* Oh, yes, OK. *(Pause)* Right, just wait a moment please. What do you want me to tell him?

He covers phone mouthpiece.

JOEL

(To CHARLIE) That was the children's hospital. I don't think they've read the papers. One of the consultants, who sounds like an amazing woman, caught your pub comedy routine the other night, and she wants to know if you will come in two nights a week, wear a clown suit, and make the kids happy.

HATTIE

(Lit up, excited and animated) There you go: Wavy Gravy.

JOEL

OK, I'll buy it. Who or what is Wavy Gravy?

HATTIE

Who. He's a clown. He works with sick kids. In America. He's a saint.

Exit. They look at each other.

A WEEK LATER

EXT. CHILDREN'S HOSPITAL: OUTSIDE—AFTERNOON

The VW bus draws up outside the hospital. CHARLIE comes out of the build-

ing in full clown gear—no changing room—including silly long shoes and red nose etc. As he gets closer we see that tears are running down his face.

INT. CAMPER VAN OUTSIDE CHILDREN'S HOSPITAL—CONTINUOUS

CHARLIE *gets into front seat. Sits there. Tears.*

JOEL *and* HATTIE *look at each other. They smile.* CHARLIE *just about manages to speak.*

CHARLIE
Thanks for picking me up.

HATTIE
Happy to—we'll take you straight home.

JOEL *drives off.*

INT. CHARLIE'S HOUSE: MUSIC ROOM—LATER

CHARLIE
Now it's time for the cinnamon toast.

HATTIE
(Kindly) Looks like we've got a broken hearted clown situation here. *(Goes over to touch him.)*

CHARLIE *sits there. Calm now. Tired.*

JOEL
(Quietly) How were you?

CHARLIE
I was really great. I was really really great. They loved me. Wait till you see the reviews.

HATTIE
What are you going to do about it?

CHARLIE
I'm going to get some sleep.

Hattie, Charlie

A good day

That's probably enough for now dear. Don't you think? Did you enjoy that? You've got a better colour. Do you want to lie down again now? I'll get Murray to come and help you. Can you manage the bathroom yourself today? Oh good. It's a good day then. I'll wait here till you're through, and then I'll get Murray to come and make sure you're comfortable. Can you say that again? Again maybe? Oh yes. Yes, thank you. I'm absolutely fine. Yes, yes—absolutely nothing to worry about. We're all really really fine.

Joel, Hattie

What he needs

—How did it go?

—It went well, I think.

—You think?

—No. I'm sure, really. Yes. He liked it.

—Did he say anything?

—No. But I could see he was listening. His greyness was less when I'd finished. I'm sure of that. Not quite pink, but definitely less grey. I can't be certain, but he sort of smiled at the outrageous bits.

—How far did you get?

—I stopped after the first visit to the children's hospital.

—Before the dream sequence?

—Yes.

—That was wise.

—Yes. It had been quite a lot for him to take. In fact I wonder if I should have stopped whilst things were jolly and not even started on the hospital scene?

—No. You got it just right. It will get things moving in his psyche.

—Should I read more today?

—No. That's enough for today. Murray will spend time with him, and Rinchen will work her magic. Let him sleep on it. Let his dream life kick in.

—This is all right, isn't it, Joel?

—It's more than all right Hattie. It's just what he needs. It's marvellous that the project is under way.

—Oh Joel. Thank God you're here.

Rinchen, Charlie

Slow and foggy

Hello Charlie. It's me. Rinchen. Can I sit close by you please? The Following Cat is here and he's guarding the door. I'm not going to talk this afternoon—well, not much—Mum said you've heard a lot of words today. So I'm going to just sit and be peaceful like Simon showed me how to. If you need anything, anything at all, let me know somehow. It's quite slow and foggy where you are, isn't it? But I don't mind. You can let me know slow and foggy. I'm not in any sort of hurry.

Hattie, Charlie

The next bit

Hello Charlie. Oh you're looking so much brighter today. Did Murray get you over here by the window? Rinchen picked these snowdrops for you and said to say good morning and she'll see you after school. She says she's got something to tell you. Where would you like the flowers? Here? Why don't I put them on the window sill for now, so you can see them at the same time as looking out of the window.

Would you like me to go on with reading the film script to you? Oh good. I'm so pleased. We need you to join us you know. Whenever you're ready. No rush. No pressure. Just wanting to let you know we want you back on the team when the time is right.

Well, here's the next bit. Joel wrote this for you from what you told him at the time. It's very beautiful, and just right, I think. Here goes . . .

Joel: filmscript 20

Charlie's dream

INT. CHARLIE'S HOUSE: CHARLIE'S ROOM—LATER

CHARLIE *has lain down on the bed and fallen asleep in his clown costume— has taken nose off—it's still in his hand; boots on floor.*

DREAM SEQUENCE

INT. CHILDREN'S HOSPITAL—MORNING

CHARLIE is in his clown suit—images of sick children—he's making them laugh. Lots of images come thick and fast and do not linger, then focus on one child.

CHILD
(Thin, bald head from chemotherapy, big dark Jewish eyes just like JOEL's)
Who are you?

CHARLIE
I'm Charlie the clown.

CHILD
No—who are you really?

CHARLIE looks at the child for a long time. CHARLIE falls into the eyes. The eyes are the eyes of the PARFAIT.

EXT. CASTLE GARDEN—CONTINUOUS

PARFAIT
Who are you?

TROUBADOUR
I am Jean-Luc Marias.

PARFAIT
And where are you?

TROUBADOUR
I am in the springtime of the world, the magic place of music, where my Lady waits and sings. The *loc aizi.*

PARFAIT
You know, don't you, that you are also in hell? The Occitan culture that allows you to sing is being systematically destroyed by the French.

TROUBADOUR
The truth of my art does not depend on circumstance. Orpheus sang in hell.

PARFAIT
True: but he lost Eurydice. The lords of hell will know how to make you look back.

TROUBADOUR

I know that they hate the Troubadours almost as much as they hate the Cathars, because they hate freedom, and they hate the truth. You must not bend—your way is straight into the fire without looking to the right or left. My way is not yours—my way is the way of disguise: I can sing different songs, but they are still the same song. I can make people laugh. I can leave the high courts and go among the people and earn my food in taverns: I can make people laugh, and, by doing that, I can open their hearts to what is.

PARFAIT

When the French come, they will destroy my religion completely. But they will do worse to your music. They will take your *fin amor*, your alchemy of love, and make it into a game for bored aristocrats.

TROUBADOUR

How do you know that?

PARFAIT

When you write a song, where does the music come from? This knowledge is the same. It comes from the same place.

TROUBADOUR

Tell me more. Tell me what you can see.

PARFAIT

I can see the death of our language and our country. I can see that my religion will vanish completely, since we write nothing down and make no monuments. Your poetry will survive, and will change the whole world, but at a cost: it will be watered down and made into a kind of game. Only a few very great poets will know what you really meant, and take the poetry further.

TROUBADOUR

That is enough: that is more than enough.

PARFAIT

And so I think it will be for our religion—I think—I pray. The form will vanish but the spirit will survive, however long it may take to revive. It may take a thousand years to shake the hold of the jealous God.

END DREAM SEQUENCE

Hattie, Joel

Always this smile

—Well. It went well.

—Good. Are you OK, Hattie?

—I think so. I was anxious before I started reading—scared it would be too much for him—but actually you could feel the atmosphere in the room lighten as we got into it. Brighter, somehow.

—There. I told you it would be all right, didn't I?

—Yes. You were right, as always, Joel.

—Is that a smile I see before me?

—Before you—after you—always, always, a smile for you. Always, always this smile.

—Sounds like a song coming on, perhaps?

—Do you know, I think it might be. I was beginning to think I'd never write another song again.

—Go, go. Make a song.

Rinchen, Charlie

Poem for you

Hello Charlie. It's Rinchen. Are you asleep? Did you like the flowers? I'm writing a poem for you, Charlie, but it's got lots and lots of words in it, so I won't tell it to you today, because you've had lots and plenty of them already, Mum says. And, actually, I'm a bit stuck for a rhyme in places. But I'll read it to you soon. I know you'll like it.

Do you need to cry a little, Charlie? That's cool with me. I'll mop you up with my special cotton hankie that came from Grandma's house. Cry lots and plenty if it will help you, Charlie. Whatever helps. Whatever.

Hattie, Joel

Tough till you get there

—We have to do some lighter scenes now, Joel, don't you think?

—Yes. It's going to take a while for him to integrate the dream sequence. But we need to keep the momentum of the story going. Keep him engaged.

—OK. What shall we do next?

—What's on the list?

—There's a lot to choose from. Supposing we do that playful time in the kitchen when I was trying to get to grips with designing that programme?

—Good idea. It was this time of year too, wasn't it? It might help him re-orientate to the here and now.

—It was January, actually.

—How do you know?

—I bought a new coat in the January sales.

—Oh, Hattie.

—I know. I know. But a girl remembers these things.

—OK. I'll buy it. What sort of coat?

—It was one of those whitish grey long shaggy things—sheepskin or goat-skin or somesuch.

—Oh, yes, I do remember it. And I remember how ridiculously happy you were to have acquired it.

—It was a great bargain. You were so funny when I showed it to you both. Trying so hard to see why Charlie and I were so enthusiastic about an article of clothing—a coat, for heaven's sake.

—You did look fantastic in it. You wore it to go to see Pasteur in Oxford, didn't you?

—Yes, that's why I remember it so well, actually—that was a tough assign-ment—till I got there.

—And isn't that always how it is, Hattie?

—Is what?

—A tough assignment till you get there?

—True, dear. True.

Hattie, Charlie

My programme plan

Hey, Charlie—I found this old coat to wear for you today. Remember? My fantastic January sales bargain of a lifetime coat? Poor Joel thought we had gone completely mad with our excitement over it. He never really understood shopping, did he? Or clothes. He did try though—remember that time we got him to try loons? And purple loons, no less. And that funny little jumper with the mushrooms embroidered on it? Actually, he looked really really beautiful. Particularly in his embarrassment. I remember you tried to teach him an appropriate walk to go with the outrageous clothes. In fact you offered him a whole selection of walks to choose from. And, dear friend that he was, he gave them all a try, one after the other, assiduously, meticulously, on the long walk into town and down Broad Street. In the rain. Oh Charlie it's good to see you smile.

Well, I'm wearing the coat to get us in the right time zone. It's 1973, we're in the kitchen in your house in Edgbaston—yes, sorry, our house in Edgbaston—and you two are trying to get me to focus on my dream radio programme. And focus is just what I'm out of. Listen to this and see what you think.

Hattie: filmscript 21

Hattie's programme plan

INT. CHARLIE'S HOUSE: KITCHEN—MORNING

January 1973.

JOEL
Hattie, I have to tell you, much as the bosses love those current affairs programmes of yours, it's really time to get back to the big project.

HATTIE
Yes, I know. I've done enough to make them love me—for now at any rate.

CHARLIE

Oh, come on, you've got Andrew and Michael eating out of your hand!

HATTIE

(Laughs)

CHARLIE

I've never seen a more outrageous bid for power, and, listen, I'm in the acting business.

HATTIE

They need it. They don't know what it is they need, but they need it.

JOEL

What do you mean?

HATTIE

I don't give a damn about making them promote me—that's a by-product, very nice, very useful, but it's not it. I could walk away from this at any moment. And what's more, they know it too. That's part of it.

JOEL

So what is it, then?

HATTIE

It's *désir*. You know that Magritte painting? The perfectly rendered night sky, a constellation of stars, and the stars are grouped to say one word: *désir*. I'm making them come alive. I make that place sing. They feel obsessed, and don't know what's happening to them. They are very happy! *(Laughs)*.

JOEL

(Concerned) How do you know you're not compromising your integrity?

HATTIE

Integrity shmegrity. They can't touch me—I'm the Gingerbread Pig.

JOEL

What on earth is a Gingerbread Pig?

HATTIE

Exactly! *(Laughs.)*

JOEL

OK, OK. And the big project?

HATTIE

I've got my first big interview set up for Friday—this Provençal expert at Oxford. It will be interesting, I know he knows the stuff, or at least he has the reputation for knowing it, but I don't know how he will handle me. I'm going to play it low key to start with, and see where his ego is. There are plenty of other academics. Either his heart's in the right place or it isn't—I'm not going to compromise on that one.

CHARLIE

Have you ever been to Oxford?

HATTIE

No, why?

CHARLIE

Do you want me to come with you?

HATTIE

(Looks at him with slightly outraged amazement) Charlie?

CHARLIE

(Backs off) OK, OK.

We see that he's not offended, but concerned about her ability to handle the upper classness of it. All this is quite understated.

JOEL

Do you have anything like an outline?

HATTIE

It begins with the dream—the dream of the Lady—the Toulouse dream.

CHARLIE

Yes, we know about the dream, but what we need is focus, my love.

HATTIE

I'm not ready for an outline yet—I'm still working on the concept, and how to describe my vision of how it's going to be; this has to be really creative radio, something no-one has done before. Not just some lightweight thing to entertain you while you're doing the ironing.

CHARLIE

Are you sure radio is the right medium?

HATTIE

Yes, yes—this is why I went into radio in the first place. The thing is—I want to push the medium to its limits, use everything it's got to offer. You can do anything in radio, because you don't have to provide the pictures, you're not tied down. It's fantastic.

CHARLIE

Cheap, too—no sets and you can double up your actors.

JOEL

But what exactly are you going to do?

HATTIE

I'm going to pick it up and run with it. Somehow—I don't yet know how—I'm going to convey the mystery.

JOEL

Are we talking about any specific mystery here?

HATTIE

(*Impatiently*) The mystery!

CHARLIE *and* JOEL *look at one another and shrug with good humour and affection—implying 'this is* HATTIE*'.*

CHARLIE

Look, If you need practical help getting this together, just let us know.

HATTIE

Thanks—appreciated. When I've got something solid you'll be the first to know.

Hattie, Murray

Kitchen show business

—Hey Murray. Good news.

—Always good to hear good news, Hat.

—Charlie is hungry.

—Hey, that really is good news! How hungry?

—Not sure. I think maybe only a little bit hungry.

—Leave it with me, gorgeous. I'll make something light but special. It'll leave him wanting more.

—Thank you.

—That's kitchen show business for you.

—No—I mean—thank you for always being here Murray. I truthfully don't know how we'd manage without you.

—No problem, Angel. I'm here for the duration.

Hattie, Charlie, Joel

The radio play

Charlie, this is the flashback you thought we needed. Well, one of them. The time when Dad and I heard that amazing radio programme together, when I was about 14. I think this might be just a rough draft. I'd like you to do the final version, really. Like you did with the Gingerbread Pig story and little Hattie. When you're better, I mean really better, you can hotseat me and find out what I was like at 14. That'll be fun. Won't it? Charlie? Charlie?

—Joel. Shall I just go ahead? His eyes are so dull today.

—Yes. It's a sweet piece. It'll touch him gently

—But I'm not sure he can hear me.

—Something in him will hear you.

—He seems far away. Farther away than ever.

—Trust me, Hattie. You will be heard.

Hattie: filmscript 22

Radio play

INT. HATTIE'S PARENTS' HOUSE: FRONT ROOM—EVENING

It's 1964. HATTIE is 14. FATHER is 46. A terraced house in Manchester— front room—impeccably tidy and well cared for—a neat working class home. Books everywhere. Saturday evening: HATTIE is all dressed up to go dancing.

FATHER
Where are you going?

HATTIE
I'm off into town. I'm meeting Megan and Alison; we're going dancing.

FATHER

But it's that radio programme I told you about; I want you to stay and listen to it with me.

HATTIE

Oh Daaad, I promised them, and everyone's going to be there.

FATHER

This is important. The first time I heard this I realised that it's what my life has been about. It's important. I want you to hear it, and I want us to hear it together.

HATTIE looks at him—she realises it's serious.

HATTIE

I'm sorry—you're right, and I forgot. I expect they'll manage without me. *She sits next to him on the sofa. They snuggle up.*

They listen to one of the Radio Ballads *created by Ewan MacColl, Peggy Seeger, and Charles Parker, about the nomads of the British Isles. We'll see if we can get permission to quote extracts.*

FATHER

My God, they did it. They got it just right.

HATTIE

That was the best thing I've ever heard. Thank you for making me stay. I think you just changed my whole life. Again. *(Laughter).*

FATHER

What is it now, then?

HATTIE

That's what I'm going to do, that's all. That's going to be my work. I can make programmes like that: I know I can.

FATHER

Do you know how hard it is to get into the BBC?

HATTIE

What I know is, that's what I'm going to do; no question. I just know it.

FATHER

You'd better get yourself what they would recognise as an education then. It will have to be University, and it had better be a good one.

HATTIE

OK, if that's what you have to do, I'll do it.

FATHER

You have to find out how the system works and how they talk to each other; you have to meet people.

HATTIE

I'll do it.

FATHER

Less dancing, more studying.

HATTIE

I'll do the studying—but I'm still going to dance! *(Laughter)*. And I'm still going to sing. I'll do what it takes, but they won't change that.

Rinchen, Murray

Heart sutra

—Mum's worried again Murray. I don't know what to do.

—What does Rinpoche say?

—He says something in Tibetan that I don't know yet.

—What happens when you hear it, Blossom?

—Am I Blossom now?

—Yes—Blossom Dearie. You can tell Charlie that. It will make him smile, I expect.

—Why will it make him smile, Murray?

—Because Blossom Dearie is a famous singer.

—Like in the opera?

—No. Not at all like in the opera. What happens when you hear it?

—I go warm and strong and there is big sunshine in my chest and everyone in the world is as beautiful as the Following Cat.

—AHA! That will be the *Heart Sutra* then?

—Will it?

—Definitely.

—Do you know the *Heart Sutra* by heart Murray?

—I do, Blossom. It's my absolute and total favourite. Shall I say it to you?

—Yes, please Murray. Come and say it to me and Charlie. Make his heart strong again, please.

Murray, Charlie, Rinchen

Prajnaparamita

Di ke dag gi tö pa dü chig na, chom den de gyal po'i khab cha gö pung po'i ri la, ge long gi gen dün chen po tang, jang chub sem pa'i gen dun chen po tang tab chig tu zhug te, de'i tse chom den de zab mo nang wa zhe ja wa chö kyi nam drang kyi ting nge dzin la nyom par zhug so.

Yang de'i tse, jang chub sem pa sem pa chen po pag pa chen re zig wang chuk she rab kyi pa rol tu chin pa zab mo chö pa nyi la nam par ta zhing, pung po nga po de dag la yang rang zhin gyi tong par nam par ta'o

De nei, sang gye kyi tü, tse dang den pa sha ri'i bü jang chub sem pa sem pa chen po pag pa chen re zig wang chuk la di ke che me so:

Rig kyi bu gang la la she rab kyi pa rol tu chin pa zab mo chö pa che par dö pa de ji tar lab par ja

Di ke che me pa dang, jang chub sem pa sem pa chen po pag pa chen re zig wang chuk gi tse dang den pa sha ra da ti'i bu la di ke che me so:

Sha ri'i bu, rig kyi bu am rig kyi bu mo gang la la she rab kyi pa rol tu chin pa zab mo chö pa che par dö pa de, di tar nam par ta war ja te, pung po nga po de dag kyang rang zhin gyi tong par nam par yang dag par je su ta'o

Zug tong pa'o. Tong pa nyi zug so. Zug le tong pa nyi zhen ma yin no. Tong pa nyi le kyang zug zhen ma yin no. De zhin du, tsor wa dang, dü she dang, dü che dang, nam par she pa nam tong pa'o.

Sha ri bu, de ta we na, chö tam che tong pa nyi de, tsen nyi me pa, ma kye pa, ma gag pa, dri ma me pa, dri ma dang dral wa me pa, dri wa me pa, gang wa me pa'o.

Sha ri'i bu, de ta we na, tong pa nyi la zug me, tsor wa me, dü she me, dü che nam me, nam par she pa me, mig me, na wa me, na me, che me, lü me, yid me, zug me, dra me, dri me, ro me, reg ja me, chö me do.

Mig gi kham me pa ne yid kyi kham me, yid kyi nam par she pa'i kham kyi bar du yang me do.

Ma rig pa me, ma rig pa ze pa me pa ne ga shi me, ga shi ze pa'i bar du yang me do.

Dug ngal wa dang, kun jung wa dang, gok pa dang, lam me, ye she me, tob pa me, ma tob pa yang me do.

Sha ri'i bu, de ta we na, jang chub sem pa nam tob pa me pa'i chir, she rab kyi pa rol tu chin pa la ten ching ne te, sem la drib pa me pe, trak pa me do. Chin chi log le shin tu de ne nya ngen le de pa'i tar chin to.

Dü sum du nam par zhug pa'i sang gye tam che kyang she rab kyi pa rol tu chin pa la ten ne, la na me pa yang dag par dzog pa'i jang chub tu ngön par sang gye so.

De ta we na, she rab kyi pa rol tu chin pa'i ngag, rig pa chen po'i ngag, la na me pa'i ngag, mi nyam pa dang nyam pa'i ngag, dug ngal tam che rab tu zhi war che pa'i ngag, mi dzün pe na den par she par ja te, she rab kyi pa rol tu chin pa'i ngag me pa:

Tayata om gate gate paragate parasamgate bodhi svaha

Sha ri'i bu, jang chub sem pa sem pa chen pö de tar she rab kyi pa rol tu chin pa zab mo la lab par ja'o.

De ne, chom den de ting nge dzin de le zheng te, jang chub sem pa sem pa chen po pag pa chen re zig wang chuk la leg so zhe ja wa jin ne, leg so leg so, rig kyi bu de de zhin no.

Rig kyi bu, de de zhin te, ji tar khyö kyi ten pa de zhin du she rab kyi pa rol tu chin pa zab mo la che par ja te, de zhin sheg pa nam kyang je su yi rang ngo.

Chom den de kyi di ke che ka tsal ne, tse dang den pa sha ri'i bu dang, jang chub sem pa sem pa chen po pag pa chen re zig wang chuk dang, tam che dang den pa'i khor de dang, lha dang, mi dang, lha ma yin dang, dri zar che pa'i jig ten yi rang te, chom den de kyi sung pa la ngön par tö do.

Form is emptiness; emptiness is form. Emptiness is nothing else but form; form is nothing else but emptiness. So also are feeling, perception, formation, and consciousness nothing else but emptiness. Thus, Shariputra, all Dharmas are emptiness. There are no qualities. There is no birth, and there are no endings. There is no impurity, and there is no purity. There is no decrease, and there is no increase. Therefore, Shariputra, in emptiness, there is no form, no feeling, no perception, no formation, no consciousness; no eye, no ear, no nose, no tongue, no body, no mind; no appearance, no sound, no smell, no taste, no touch, no Dharmas, no ignorance, no end of ignorance; there is no old age and death, no cessation of old age and death; no suffering, no origin of suffering, no cessation of suffering, no path, no wisdom, no attainment, and no non-attainment. Therefore, Shariputra, since the Bodhisattvas, the wisdom beings, are completely empty of attainment, they stay through the practice of *prajnaparamita*.

Since there is no clouding of the mind, there is no fear. They transcend falsity and attain complete *nirvana*. All the Buddhas of the three eras, by means of *prajnaparamita*, fully awaken to unsurpassable, true, complete enlightenment. Therefore, the great mantra of *prajnaparamita*, the mantra of great insight, the unsurpassed mantra, the unequalled mantra, the mantra that calms all suffering, should be known as truth, since there is no deception. The *prajnaparamita* mantra is said in this way:

OM GATE GATE PARAGATE PARASAMGATE BODHI SOHA

Thus, Shariputra, the Bodhisattva Mahasattva, the majestic wisdom being, should train in the profound *prajnaparamita*.

Hattie, Charlie

Such friends

Here we are. Fresh flowers handpicked by your little one. She says she's almost ready to read you her poem. And she says to ask if you liked the *Heart Sutra?* Oh Charlie. Oh Charlie. Please come home.

Well, a postcard arrived from Ariel this morning. It's a nice photograph of the Municipal Art Gallery in Dublin. We shall go and visit Ireland when you're better. Shall we? I remember a totally brilliant gig in Dublin once—when Crazy Wisdom Lady was still small—just you, me, and Joel. It must have been the winter of 1972. We played in that strange castle place. It was a ball of some sort. Classy. Just outside Dublin, near the sea. A wild wild place. And then in town the next day. Grafton street pubs. Guinness black and silky smooth, like we'd never known before. And we came back by plane because they'd treated us so well and we wanted to celebrate. And there were smoked salmon sandwiches on the plane. Joel couldn't believe it. Economy class and smoked salmon sandwiches.

Anyway, here's what Ariel has written:

"'Say where man's glory most begins and ends

And say my glory was I had such friends.'

yours in love and friendship AKA"

Yeats, of course. It ties in nicely with that piece of yours where you do the conversation with your Grandfather. Do you remember writing that? Just before Christmas? Just before—this?

I've got some new scenes to read you today. Joel's written them. They're really beautiful. So very Joel. It's a little sequence from the time when he was working as a hospital porter. So, after graduation and after he's told his parents. After the wedding and all of that. Whilst you were in rehearsal for *The Tempest*, I guess. Here you are dear. Enjoy. Enjoy. Please.

Joel: filmscript 23

Joel the porter

MONTAGE: JOEL AS HOSPITAL PORTER.

Autumn 1971

JOEL *turning up for the job, getting uniform, etc.*

Getting shouted at by doctors and nurses. Just takes it. They think he must be stupid, because he doesn't say anything.

He makes mistakes, because you do. For instance:

JOEL *with huge load of bedpans—gazing at confusing signposts—going up and down stairs in attempt to get to ward 1E—accidentally pushing patient into broom-cupboard— etc.*

INT. HOSPITAL: CORRIDOR—AFTERNOON

A long corridor: JOEL *is pushing a middle aged woman down a corridor in a wheelchair.*

WOMAN

I'm so worried, I'm really really worried.

JOEL

What are you worried about?

WOMAN

About my husband—how will he manage while I'm here? About my daughter—her marriage is going wrong. I'm worried about my job—will they keep it open? And, will I get better?

JOEL

(Stops pushing wheelchair—puts brake on with some difficulty—comes round to face woman—bends at the knee so that he's not towering above her. His face is really kind) As I understand it, there are two types of things you can worry about. On the one hand, there are things you can do something about—in which case you stop worrying and do it. On the other hand, there are things you can do nothing about—in which case, worrying doesn't help—so you could stop worrying.

WOMAN

That's easy for you to say, young man.

JOEL

Wait there!

WOMAN

I'm not planning on going anywhere. *(She's grudgingly amused at this point).*

JOEL rushes to a side ward and picks up a big (clean!) portable urinal. He comes back, and puts in surprised woman's lap.

JOEL

I'm not taking you an inch further until you dump all of your worries into this. Then I promise you I will take them and flush them down the toilet.

WOMAN

Really, you can do that?

JOEL

Yes, and it's on the National Health.

She looks at him. She is completely won over by the strength of his stance—sees a glow around him. She laughs, makes pretend sick noises into the urinal. He disappears with bowl. Flushing noises off. Laughter from them both as he returns.

JOEL

(Taking brake off wheelchair—holding handles again and leaning in close to speak quietly into her right ear.) We are so late! Mr Brandon is going to have my guts for garters! One thing you don't do is keep a consultant waiting; it cuts into their private earning time. How do you fancy the roller coaster route?

WOMAN
Yes, yes, have a go.

He sets off pushing wheel chair and running down the empty corridor—farcical rough ride, up and down corridors, ramps, etc. Laughter. At one point they come into an area where there are other people, so JOEL slows down and they both act serious—then burst into giggles as they turn the corner into a more deserted corridor.

INT. HOSPITAL: SINGLE ROOM—EVENING

View from window shows it to be early evening, JOEL is taking an elderly man back to his bed. Puts him to bed. He is in this room by himself.

JOEL
OK, I'll say goodnight.

MAN
Do you have to go just yet?

JOEL
No, no, I don't.

MAN
Will you sit with me a while? I'm very frightened.

JOEL
Yes of course—where would you like me to sit?

MAN
Beside the bed?

JOEL
Sure. *(He sits.)*

MAN
Will you hold my hand?

JOEL takes his hand and the man relaxes.

MONTAGE: JOEL SITTING BY PATIENT

Quick fire stills show time passing—music on soundtrack—they go through the night—JOEL shifting about—sits by the bed, then on the bed, then kneels by the man's side—at first the man is talking and talking—falls asleep, eventually—wakes intermittently and sees JOEL is still there—awake—so man goes back to sleep reassured.

INT. HOSPITAL: SINGLE ROOM—MORNING

View through window shows it's early morning. NURSE *enters.*

NURSE

(Hearty, loud, and cheerful) Good morning, Mr O'Leary—time to wake up—another beautiful day!

She stops short when she sees JOEL.

NURSE

Joel, for goodness sake what are you doing here? You should have gone home at 6 o'clock last night!

JOEL

Mr O'Leary is a friend of mine.

NURSE

There are visiting times for that sort of thing.

JOEL

Not in the night. The night is when you need a friend.

He gets up to go.

JOEL

Oh, and you might find it a little hard to wake Mr O'Leary.

JOEL *goes out of the door.*

March 2004

Hattie, Joel

Lifeline

—Well, Joel.

—Welcome Hattie.

—Shall I try again?

—Keep going, Hattie. Just keep going.

—It's getting harder to just keep going. There hasn't been much change recently.

—I heard a wonderful story when I was a child. It moved me very deeply.

—OK. Tell me.

—It concerned a man who'd been in hospital, in a deep coma, for thirty years. One day he inexplicably woke up. As people do.

—Do they?

—They do. Trust me. They do. But here's the touching bit. His best friend had visited him every single day without fail, all through the thirty years, and had read him that day's newspaper. Not knowing whether he was being heard or not. No sign. And it turned out that the man in the coma had heard and understood every word. Those daily visits were his lifeline.

—OK, Joel. We keep going. However long it takes.

—Exactly.

Hattie, Charlie

Oxford trip

Hello, my dear. It's another fine day. Do you want to sit up? Not to worry. You stay lying down if you prefer. It's just it might do you good to have a change of view. Rinchen and Annabel are playing outside—some make-believe game. They are very sweet to watch. Well. Maybe later. Maybe this afternoon. They're going down to the little wood to fetch you a huge bunch of daffodils, I believe. Everything's so early this year. Can you hear the blackbird? The sweet sound of an English spring.

Joel sends his love. We've been busy writing some more of the film script—though re-defining the genre somewhat. You'll have to help us get the text sorted properly when it comes to rewriting and editing. But this will do for now. It's good that the list on the kitchen notice board is getting shorter. Rinchen is still crossing things off (with panache!) for us, as the scenes get written. It seems strange now to look at that marvellous letter you sent her about panache—just days before—before this. She's pinned it to the notice board. I think it helps her.

Anyway, here's the next piece for you. Can you hear me if I sit just here? Do you need me to sit closer? Well, I think I will, anyway. Oh Charlie, I hope I'm not crowding you. Can you give me any sort of sign? Oh good. Thank you. Shall I read to you now? OK. Here you are, then. It starts with that first trip of mine to Oxford. Goodness me, I had a nerve, didn't I? And I had no idea that you and Joel were so worried about me. Not till later, anyway. It was fun.

Hattie: filmscript 24

Oxford trip

EXT. CHRIST CHURCH MEADOW—AFTERNOON

February 1973. We follow HATTIE; *she is coming up to the back of Christ Church College, from Christ Church Meadow. Snow on ground. Crocuses showing through the snow. Bright sunshine—all very beautiful.*

We follow her through the college gates, and across the quad to a staircase. She is wearing a white sheepskin coat, a beautiful stylish woolly hat, long scarf, colourful, slightly chaotic looking long skirt. Big boots. She is carrying recording equipment in a bag. Equipment appropriate for 1973: it's a big bag.

INT. OXFORD COLLEGE: STAIRCASE OUTSIDE PROFESSOR PASTEUR'S ROOM—
CONTINUOUS

Stone corridor. Old. HATTIE *is about to knock on an imposing door; we realise that this is one of the few occasions when she is not fully in command of the situation. Touches Gingerbread Pig amulet (which she always wears round her neck) for luck. She notices someone has carved their name on the door, rather low down: she kneels to look at it. It says 'Byron'.*

HATTIE
(To herself, quietly) Fuck.

Before she can get back to her feet, the door opens. She looks up: PROFESSOR PASTEUR *looks down.*

PROFESSOR PASTEUR
It's a forgery.

HATTIE *smiles, and stands up.*

PASTEUR *has a hat and coat on, he is clearly on his way somewhere.*

HATTIE
Hattie; Hattie Tattersall from the BBC.

PASTEUR
From the BBC?

HATTIE
Yes, my PA fixed up an appointment for me to see you.

PASTEUR
What's a PA?

HATTIE
(Laughs) Ah. It's a personal assistant.

PASTEUR
Really, how interesting. You have a personal assistant all of your own? Is that like a verger?

HATTIE
What's a verger?

They both laugh.

PASTEUR

I think we're going to get on well, once we establish a common vocabulary. Do, please, come in.

INT. OXFORD COLLEGE: PROFESSOR PASTEUR'S ROOM—CONTINUOUS

Books everywhere—small table with sherry in a decanter and glasses under the window. We're quite high up in the building—snow scene out of the window, beautiful; it's a nice view, including trees and river. Late morning.

PASTEUR lets her in; a slightly embarrassed kerfuffle about who brings in the bag.

He courteously pulls out a chair from the table in the middle of the room and she sits. He removes hat and coat.

PASTEUR

Would you like some sherry?

HATTIE

No thanks.

He makes some space on the table—moving the piles of old books and stacking them up on other piles of old books around the room—so she can put her recording equipment down somewhere.

HATTIE

As I said in my letter *(he looks puzzled)*. My letter?

He gestures: 'Continue'.

HATTIE

I'm writing and producing a radio documentary about Occitania. I've read both your books, but what I need from you for the programme is the basic information clearly spelled out. The subject of the programme is this: there were two things going on in Twelfth Century Occitania: the Troubadour phenomenon, and the Cathar phenomenon. When I switch the tape recorder on, could you please give a short clear account of what those two movements meant, and how important they were?

PASTEUR

I'll do my best, I'm not known for my brevity.

HATTIE

(Laughs) That's all right—I'm known for my editing.

She sets up her recording equipment—she is extremely competent with the machinery. She is looking down at it. Then she puts the microphone in front of him.

HATTIE

OK—testing for levels. Please say something into the microphone.

PASTEUR

(Leaning down into the microphone—he is not competent with the machinery) 'Your laughter is like the laughter of God'.

HATTIE *recognises the quotation (note to self: check source). She looks up at him in clear delight. There is a charming rapport between them—warm but not in any way flirtatious. They are, in their different ways, very much on the same wavelength.*

HATTIE

You don't mess about, do you? I knew I'd come to the right place. Most people say 'Mary had a little lamb'.

(He laughs.)

HATTIE

She repeats 'Your laughter is like the laughter of God' in Provençal. (Need a subtitle here).

PASTEUR

Ah, my dear, you have been to the beautiful place.

Fresh camera angle here—facing window—sunlight coming through—enhanced atmosphere for a held moment or two. Camera tight on HATTIE'S *face: for a moment, she has the 12c* LADY's *face: all done by facial expression, no special effects.*

PASTEUR *sees something, and smiles. You get the sense that he too understands the big picture.*

HATTIE

(As her present day self) Right: ready when you are.

PASTEUR *crosses the room to sit by the window and starts to talk. He is looking out of the window on to a snowy Oxford scene.*

Camera follows out of the window and moves into a depiction of 12c Provence via flowers—the springtime of the world. As the Professor speaks the following, the camera depicts everyday life in 12c Provence—Troubadours and Cathars and ordinary people; happiness: grainy, dirty, vivid. There is

Troubadour music.

PASTEUR

At the beginning of Europe, in the springtime of the world, a set of travel-ling singers in the south of France—except it wasn't then France—set the agenda for the poetic and emotional life of Europe. What is our poetry about? It is about love. Why is this? Because the Troubadour poets of 12c Occitania decided that it should be so. And no-one, ever since, in any of the languages and literatures of Europe, has much contradicted that.

HATTIE

What do you mean by love?

PASTEUR

Some say they got it from the Arabs, from the Sufi poets, through their contact with Spain. Love meant two things, and only one thing. It meant desire, and joy. It meant being driven by desire to a strange beautiful place, to another level of being, to that transcendence, where desire consumes itself and there is only joy. Only joy.

Camera back in Professorial room again—focus on HATTIE.

HATTIE

Ah! Rumi…

She is excited by being with this man's mind: she quotes:

HATTIE (CONT.)

> When a man and a woman become one
> That One is You.
> And when that One becomes zero
> There You are.
> You made my lover and me
> So that you might play
> A game of love with Yourself.

PASTEUR

(Repeats a few words in Parsee) Exactly, my dear. Exactly. That's where it comes from.

PASTEUR (CONT.)

At the same time as these masters of words were creating the lyric poem in this gorgeous civilisation, in this language made for song, so rich in rhyme, in paradox, in irony; at the same time a new religion was coming to life.

MONTAGE: AS THE PROFESSOR SPEAKS

We see stained glass images: suffering, a medieval hell.

PASTEUR

They believed that this world is hell. They believed that the God that made it is the devil. The God of the Old Testament, with his vengeful aspect, his terrible temper, his propensity to cause harm, they thought was a dreadful accident, a hi-jacking of creation. Infinitely above and beyond him is God himself, pure spirit. At some terrible time in the past, some bits of this pure spirit were trapped into existence in hell as sentient beings, and forced to be reborn endlessly, endlessly, in this suffering world. A volunteer angel led a rescue mission, to bring the truth of the sprit to the beings trapped in suffering. On earth he is called Jesus. The God of this world, the Devil, had him crucified, but before this could happen the angel passed on the secret: the way out. They called it the *consolamentum*: the secret of the joyful death. A direct transmission, so they believed, from Jesus himself: a reminder of who you really are: that you are pure sprit. Once you've had this reminder, the world has no power over you. You are free; completely free.

As the above text develops, the stained glass montage builds up and then becomes centred on a crucifixion image; at first there is light through glass, but then we move through the glass into the light itself.

PASTEUR

The priests of this religion that had no priests were called by outsiders 'perfects'—'*parfaits*'—but they called themselves only this: good men, good women.

We see more realistic images of pairs of parfaits doing their everyday work and meeting with people.

PASTEUR

They travelled about earning a living as healers or weavers or carpenters, but what they brought was the *consolamentum*, the transmission from Jesus, and they would give this freely to anyone who genuinely asked for it.

CAMERA BACK IN PROFESSOR'S ROOM

PASTEUR

Of course, the church was not very happy about this phenomenon, particularly when it came to be very popular. So, they wiped it out. Systematically, and with unbelievable cruelty, torturing, burning: destroying, as they went, the entire Occitan culture—Troubadours, Cathars, the language itself; gone. God, they said, told them to do it. God told them to burn the good men and women at the stake.

As he finishes speaking he turns away from the window and towards HATTIE, *who has been sitting by the fire.*

The camera follows his gaze, and takes in HATTIE; *it then goes into the fire, and then back into 12c. Someone is being burned at the stake. The soundtrack is the Provençal song.*

EXT. OXFORD STATION—LATER

HATTIE *is talking on the phone. She is animated, and very happy.*

INT. CHARLIE'S HOUSE: KITCHEN—CONTINUOUS

CHARLIE

(On the phone) Fantastic, well done, see you later. *Puts down phone.*

JOEL *is hovering anxiously.*

CHARLIE

She says, he's got the big picture.

JOEL

Thank goodness!

Pours wine. Camera on wine glass.

Hattie, Charlie

Sleep my love

There you are dear. I'll leave you to sleep for a while now. Murray will be here for the next hour or so. I have to see to some household things—nothing important. I'll be back soon. You sleep, my love. Sleep sleep.

Hattie, Rinchen

Eat now

—Hey, sweetheart. Have you had a good time with Annabel? Is she staying for lunch?

—Yes thanks and no thanks also.

—OK. Are you ready to eat now?

—Yes please. You too, please. You didn't eat much yesterday.

—You've been talking to Joel. I recognise that foodie talk.

—Yes of course I have.

—Good.

—We think you should be outside more. It's springtime. It's good.

—I know, sweetheart. But I don't like to. I don't like to leave Charlie.

—But we're here, Mum. Me and Murray and Joel and the Following Cat and Rinpoche once removed

—Once removed? Like cousins?

—More like brothers, actually.

—Well maybe I'll go down to the water garden for a little while. You'll come and find me if Charlie needs me?

—Obviously. Eat, eat now.

Rinchen, Charlie

Gold fish

Hey hey Charlie. Look at this big jug of daffodils. And I got you some pussy willow. I'll put it here where you can touch it if you want to. I'm going to sit quietly by you now. I've got some thinking to do. But you can interrupt me anytime you want to. The Following Cat brought in a big gold fish this morning. Murray thought it came from someone's pond and it was worth a lot of money. Though not once it was dead, obviously. We said *om ah hung* and wished it a happier rebirth next time round, and did like Rinpoche said and wished all fish everywhere total liberation from samsara, except I think perhaps that's what you do when you eat something, maybe. Well, it seemed like a good thing to do even though we weren't eating the poor golden fish. The Following Cat wasn't interested in eating it either so Murray and me we decided that he had brought it to us to get lots of prayers said for fish and that maybe this fish had taken Bodhisattva vows sometime in a previous incarnation and that that was a good thing. But that's what I need to think about excuse me Charlie so I'll be quiet now and think. But I really don't mind if you interrupt me. In fact I'd quite like that. I'd quite like that a lot. Actually.

Hattie, Charlie

The crystal and the mirror

Now here's a really magical piece for you, Charlie. I'm so glad you're sitting up today. Can I make you more comfortable? Say again, darling—I didn't quite catch that. Yes. Yes. We are enjoying the writing. Very much. Pardon? Try again. Yes, you'll help us soon. Very soon. You get well now. Then we can write it together again. Are you OK with me reading now? Good. Good.

So here we are—that gorgeous and bizarre business meeting that you and Joel set up for me—and then—well, then there was that amazing realization. Right there and then in our kitchen. Extraordinary. I hope we've done it justice. I can remember it as clearly as yesterday. It's like a mobile of coloured glass spinning in perpetual motion in the sunlight. Here we go . . .

Hattie, Joel: filmscript 25

Crystal, mirror

INT. CHARLIE'S HOUSE: KITCHEN—MORNING

April 1973. HATTIE *is sitting at the kitchen table with a big pot of coffee, a flip chart pad, books, piles of paper, tapes. Early morning sunshine streaming in. She is in pyjamas—she has been up all night working on her plan for the radio programme. Enter* JOEL *and* CHARLIE—*wearing suits and ties.*

CHARLIE

Ah, Miss Smith, so glad you could make this meeting; we're very interested in your idea.

JOEL comes forward and shakes her hand. She laughs—she isn't expecting this. JOEL repeats CHARLIE's intonation on a swanee whistle. Laughter.

HATTIE

Thank you so much for sparing the time. I'm really looking forward to sharing my thoughts with you. I hope I'm not dressed too informally?

CHARLIE

Well, we'll overlook the dress code this once. *He puts his feet on the table and we see that he is wearing big clown shoes.*

JOEL

OK, Miss Smith, we do like to cut to the chase: sell us your idea.

HATTIE

I keep having these dreams. Very strong dreams. Big dreams, you might say.

JOEL

Ah, dreams are my speciality—we can interpret any dream for a small fee. Tell us your dream. *His bow tie starts to flash on and off.*

CHARLIE

Or would you like the interpretation first? Save time all round?

HATTIE

No, I'm serious: these are big dreams.

JOEL

OK, we're serious too. Tell us about them.

HATTIE

Imagine you're in 12th century Provence. The same place as my Toulouse dream. The garden in the springtime of the world. Birdsong, sunlight, flowers, greenery...

DREAM SEQUENCE

EXT. CASTLE GARDEN—MORNING

A spring day. The LADY, the TROUBADOUR, and the PARFAIT are standing together.

BEATRITZ

You give me a choice: two paths. The way of sacrifice, and the way of desire. Both have in them music and fire. And both, I know, can lead me to the truth. Should I choose?

They remain silent, looking at her.

The PARFAIT *reaches into a breast pocket and takes out a mirror. It flashes at the camera—a blinding light; he gives it to her.*

PARFAIT
What do you see?

BEATRITZ
I see nothing. Nothing but light. *(It is reflecting sunlight into her eyes.)* It dazzles my eyes.

PARFAIT
And what do you know?

BEATRITZ
I know I am nothing. The light dazzles my mind.

She hands it back to him.

PARFAIT
Keep it. You will need it.

TROUBADOUR
Takes out a crystal prism: holds it up to the light. It creates a rainbow.
What do you see?

BEATRITZ
I see everything. All the colours of light.

TROUBADOUR
And what do you know?

BEATRITZ
I know I am everything. My mind is all the colours of the light.

TROUBADOUR
Keep it. You will need it.

She is holding the crystal in one hand and the mirror in the other.

END DREAM SEQUENCE

INT. CHARLIE'S HOUSE: KITCHEN—CONTINUOUS

Camera pans around the room: catches mirrors, crystals, sunlight.

The three of them look at each other; have they been dreaming the same dream? Recognition lights up their faces. After a moment's hesitation, they move into the following dialogue, bringing their past and their present together.

CHARLIE
And the skylark, Lady?

HATTIE
Still singing, both songs.

JOEL
Joy and pain?

HATTIE
Joy and pain both.

Light builds and flashes and dazzles in the kitchen.

INT. CHARLIE'S HOUSE. MUSIC ROOM—SAME EVENING

HATTIE, CHARLIE, and JOEL are playing and singing.

one mind
one song
one dream
we are making
one mind
one song
one dream

one mind
one song
one dream
we are making
one mind
one song
one dream

this dream that you are dreaming
is the truth that I remember
and the pictures in my mind
recall the wonder of it all
and this dream that I am dreaming
is the truth that you remember
and the pictures in your mind
recall the wonder, yes the wonder of us all

hold the mirror steady

let the past show its face
hold the mirror image ready
let us each embrace
the song that we remember
the time that we recall
and the wonder, yes the wonder of it all

one mind
one song
one dream
we are making
one mind
one song
one dream

one mind
one song
one dream
we are making
one mind
one song
one dream

The song makes it clear that the three of them have been tapping into the same dream source, dreaming the same dream. Remembering a shared past, or, possibly, creating a shared past.

Hattie, Joel

Trust the process

—Joel? Joel?

—Hattie, my dear.

—Oh Joel, I thought you'd gone.

—No. I'm here. I'm not going anywhere but here.

—Sorry. I'm jumpy.

—You need more rest, Hattie. More fresh air. More foo-

—Don't you dare say it! Rinchen's more than enough. I detect the Joel Cohen school of mothering is entering her education big time.

—Well, no harm in that—especially if it brings you out in a smile.

—Sorry. I'm letting it get to me a bit.

—Have you spoken to Rinpoche?

—I've tried. He's away teaching in Seattle, or somewhere. I don't like to bother him.

—Hattie. Call Rinpoche.

—OK. When he's back in Colorado. I know the set-up there. I know when it's a good time to call.

—How did Charlie respond to the piece about the shared memory?

—I'm not sure. He might have been blocking it out in some way.

—I think not, Hattie.

—Not?

—Not. I'm beginning to see the wisdom of this strange state he's in.

—Are you? Tell me.

—Wait and see. Trust the process.

Hattie, Charlie

Consolamentum

Rinchen's made some special juice for you, Charlie. She got up early before school. It's apple juice and squished ginger and a mystery ingredient that smells very exotic. I think it's something precious that Rinpoche gave her when he was here last. Shall I hold the cup for you? Your hand is shaking rather a lot today darling. Let me help you. There. There you go.

Are you ready for the next piece? I wrote the Oxford bits, and Joel wrote the twelfth century bits—till right near the end. The last bit's mine. They fit together really well I think. See what you think when you hear them.

Hattie, Joel: filmscript 26

The consolamentum

EXT. OXFORD—MORNING

HATTIE and PASTEUR are walking round Oxford.

Camera lingers on medieval bits of Oxford; a feeling that you don't know which century you are in.

They return to PASTEUR's *room for the recording. It's one week after the last interview. Snow gone; different clothes.*

HATTIE

I could do with some material about the *consolamentum*. Explain it to me as if I knew nothing about it.

PASTEUR

The first thing you have to understand is that all that we know about the Cathars is based on interviews under the threat of torture. We cannot trust that they told the truth about religion.

HATTIE

But weren't the Parfaits completely committed to telling the truth?

PASTEUR

Yes, of course; and they did. But they were also committed to silence. The details of the main rituals, particularly the *consolamentum*, were secret. They wouldn't lie, but for the same reason they wouldn't reveal anything important. They knew that they would die at the stake and were reconciled to it. Therefore they could not be threatened. So all of the details of the rituals that we have come from ignorant people who were telling the Inquisition what they thought they wanted to know; people who would say anything to avoid the threat of extreme pain. Just as I would. So the accounts of the ritual of the consolation are disappointing. Words were said. A book was held to the consoled person's head. The Lord's prayer was recited. As far as we know, that's it. But that cannot have been it, because we also know that those who were consoled died in bliss. Showed extraordinary fortitude faced with extreme pain. They went singing into the fire. Often voluntarily; all it needed was to renounce the heresy, and their lives would be spared. When the siege of Montségur ended, it is said the fires were waiting at the foot of the hill, and the besieged came down the steep track singing and without hesitation walked into the flames that were waiting for them. Many of those who did that were not Cathars until that morning; such was the radiance and tranquillity of those about to die that many converted and accepted the flames on the spot. To burn to death in that company, with that energy of love, was better than anything that life could offer. Where it happened, so they say, a laurel tree now grows, and the valley is full of peace.

HATTIE

What was the *consolamentum*?

PASTEUR

This was the key to the whole thing. It was the transmission, believed to have come directly from Jesus himself, in fact believed to have been the entire point of Jesus's journey to earth, that would set us free. Like Buddhists and Hindus they believed that we reincarnate constantly, from birth to birth, through lives as humans or animals, until we can find a way out from rebirth in hell. The *consolamentum* ritual was the way out. Once you had received it, you were committed to very strict vows of truth, chastity, dietary laws, and so on; if you kept those laws then you would die joyfully and go straight to God.

HATTIE

If you failed to keep them?

PASTEUR

Then you were automatically unconsoled, and back to square one. And what's more had you consoled anyone else, they too would also be unconsoled. Very serious. So most people chose to be consoled at the point of dying, when it was much easier to keep the vows. Only the Parfaits, who must have been motivated by a desire to pass on the transmission to as many as possible, and to save people from the pains of death, and also by a knowledge that they had the courage to keep the vows; only they took them when they might expect to live long enough to have them tested.

HATTIE

At some point when I'm editing this, I'll need to know exactly what the words mean: 'Parfait', and 'Cathar'.

PASTEUR

Right. 'Parfait' is a French translation of the Latin *perfectus* (or *perfecta*, the feminine: women were called Parfaites). And it means of course 'perfect'. But, here's the problem: that's not what they called themselves. That's an Inquisition word. We don't know what they called themselves. The people simply called them 'the good men, the good women'. It's the same with 'Cathar'. A Cathar is a believer in the religious system that I've described to you, but that's an Inquisition term too. Its origin, so scholars think, comes from a word meaning cat-lover. Who knows? What did they call themselves? 'Good Christians'.

HATTIE

The position of women?

PASTEUR

Equal, as far as we can tell. The soul has no gender, and can be reborn as an animal or human of either sex, and all of us have experienced all of the variations. Gender is a temporary thing. Meaningless in the eyes of God; in fact, actually, worse than that because strictly gender is an invention of the devil, as are all of the circumstances of existence. Anything dualistic is of the devil. Perhaps, perhaps, that's what happened in the *consolamentum*: perhaps the experience of transcendence, of knowing our real nature, was given: a unity beyond any dualism. Perhaps. Don't quote me on that. *(Laughter)*.

INT. CASTLE: BEATRITZ' MUSIC ROOM—NIGHT

Candlelight—the PARFAIT *giving instruction to the* LADY *again. There is knocking at the door—a maid shows in a young man from the village.*

MAN

My Lady, I am so sorry to disturb you, and the good man here, I really beg your pardon, but it is most urgent.

BEATRITZ

I am sorry for your distress. Please: say what you need to say.

MAN

Lady, it is my mother. She is dying. She wishes to see the good man before she dies. She longs to be consoled. *To* PARFAIT. Please, sir, will you come?

PARFAIT

Of course. How near death is she?

MAN

Very near. Her body is very weak, and the light of her spirit is dim.

PARFAIT

Can she understand?

MAN

Oh, yes, her mind is quite clear. She is known for her good mind in the village. Please, please come.

PARFAIT

(To BEATRITZ) Lady, please excuse me: this is my work.

BEATRITZ

Of course. You must go at once.

PARFAIT

I think you should come too. I think this is a time for you to learn something.

EXT. OXFORD: ABOUT THE CITY—AFTERNOON

HATTIE and PASTEUR are walking and talking, as before.

HATTIE

But didn't the Catholic Church offer extreme unction to the dying?

PASTEUR

No. They brought that in specifically as a response to, and imitation of, Cathar ritual. Not many people know that.

EXT. CASTLE: PATH TO VILLAGE—NIGHT

The PARFAIT and the LADY and the MAN are making their way to the village—it is wet, cold, windy. They are cloaked up. A sense of secrecy about it. Secrecy and urgency.

INT. PEASANT COTTAGE—NIGHT

Middle aged WOMAN, clearly dying, on bedding near fire place. Various people around. Sadness, but not weeping and wailing. The WOMAN is in pain but handling it.

Enter the PARFAIT with the LADY (disguised by her cloak) and the MAN. LADY stays in background, hooded.

The PARFAIT takes charge.

PARFAIT

(To dying woman) Daughter, do you sincerely want me to be here? Are you absolutely sure?

WOMAN

Oh yes, sir, oh yes: thank you, thank you.

PARFAIT

(Takes the woman's hand) All is well now my dear, all is very well.

She smiles, painfully.

PARFAIT

(To the others in the room) Please clear the room. My assistant will stay.
He is sharp and firm.

Candlelight, firelight. He is kneeling by her bedside.

PARFAIT

Do you wish to be received into the Church of God, daughter?

WOMAN

With all my heart.

PARFAIT

I will give you the vows: they are very strict and you must not break
them for all of the rest of your life. This is very important. Do you understand?

WOMAN

For all that remains of my life, however long or short, I will keep the vows
of the Church of God.

PARFAIT

Do you swear it on this book, the Book of God?

WOMAN

I swear; I swear.

*The PARFAIT begins to chant quietly in Occitan. He has the book in his
hand placed on the top of her head. His other hand is holding hers. We see
peace begin to come into her face.*

PARFAIT

Now, daughter, listen carefully please. This is the *consolamentum*. This is
our baptism. It is not the baptism of water: it is the baptism of fire. You
will receive the fire of the spirit. I have the power to transmit it to you
directly. This fire is real. You will experience it as burning heat. Do not
resist it. Let it in. Are you ready for this, my daughter?

WOMAN

Sir, I am frightened. All my life I have been frightened of fire.

PARFAIT

Trust me. Follow me. Come with me: we will go into the fire together,
and meet God.

They are in front of the fire in the chimney, they seem to go right into the white hot heat together.

Cut to LADY: *she can see this. Her eyes widen. She makes a move to go forward, then realises they don't need help. The* PARFAIT *may even put out hand to stop her.*

Cut to brilliant white heat of the fire. PARFAIT *and* WOMAN *emerge: they are back sitting as they were.*

The woman opens her eyes: they are brilliant blue. The spirit shines through them.

She tries, and fails, to speak.

PARFAIT

Don't even try to find words. You have seen God. You have been through the fire. You know: now, you simply know. You are free. Now you may go directly to God.

She leans back against the pillows, completely relaxed, eyes closed, smiling. She nods. Her smile increases, becomes a gape of wonder and joy. There is light. She dies.

Camera pans to LADY'*s face. Reaction.*

PARFAIT

Now you can see why we are not afraid of the fire.

EXT. CASTLE GARDEN—MORNING

BEATRITZ *is in the garden—it is after she has witnessed the* consolamentum. *She has the death scene in mind. She holds up a small mirror, sunlight glances off mirror, she goes through the mirror into the white light. Comes out laughing and crying.*

BEATRITZ
It's so simple—so simple.

Hattie, Joel

Dreaming

—He was trying to tell me something, Joel. I have no idea what it was though.

—Did he like the script?

—I'm pretty sure he did. Yes.

—And now?

—He's asleep. Fast asleep. Deeper than usual. Do you think that's all right?

—Yes. Yes I do. He's dreaming.

—How do you know?

—Trust me. I'm an expert.

—Joel Cohen—what happened to that shy modest young man I used to know and love?

—Shy and modest proved no longer useful. Used to?

—I know you even better now. And love you even more.

—Me too. Me you too.

Rinchen, Hattie

Perchance to dream

—Did you give Charlie the Dharma medicine, Mum?

—I did, sweetheart.

—And the juice?

—And the juice.

—Did he like it?

—He did. Definitely did.

—Did he go to sleep perchance to dream?

—Yes, precious. Did Charlie give you that line?

—Previous Charlie did. Perchance is a good word isn't it?

—I think perchance it is.

—And did you phone Rinpoche like Joel told you to?

—How did you know that?

—Joel told me and told me to check.

—You two are ganging up on me. I shall have to watch my step.

—We're ganging up for you Mum. And we will watch your step. Did you call Rinpoche?

—Yes, I did actually.

—And what did he say?

—He was very very kind and reminded me gently of the suffering we make for ourselves by clinging to attachment and aversion.

—Or indifference. Don't forget the indifference.

—You're right. Thank you.

—Do you know the not good not bad meditation?

—Is that something Rinpoche taught you precious?

—No. It's something I made up for myself. At least I think I did. Maybe I didn't. Doesn't matter. It works.

—What do you do?

—I sit with ordinary mind and anything that comes I say 'not good not bad' to. And then, after a bit of time, ordinary mind goes quieter and so I just say over and over 'not good not bad not good not bad' over and over again. And then ordinary mind somersaults and backflips and walks up walls.

—And is that good?

—It's so beyond good there are no words to say it how it is.

—I know some words.

—What are they?

—Gingerbread Pig.

—Cool! What's a Gingerbread Pig?

April 2004

Jack: letter

No regrets

Dearest daughter

This is not an easy letter to write. Please prepare yourself, dear Comrade. I have cancer. I got the results of the tests today. There is no doubt, and no cure; in any case, I know what the cure does to you before it kills you. The cancer is now in my brain and it will not be long before I become unable to bear the pain without a constant and increasing supply of morphine, and intensive nursing. This is an obvious waste of the state's resources. I am telling you this straight and clear because that is how it is between us. Truth is important.

I have had a good life. I came near to death and worse in Spain; my life since then has always seemed like a gift, to be used as fully and gratefully as possible. I have tried to live as if socialism was already here, as if we lived already in the necessity of brotherhood and comradeship. No regrets. Some sadness, but no regrets.

Much of that goodness comes from my relationship with you. I remember our joy when you were born; that joy has simply increased. I could not have imagined your life, your talent, your power and kindness, you are more than I dreamed, a limitless good fortune.

Live well, be kind, fight for others. As you always have done. I leave you my love.

I have barbiturates and some very good whisky, which I have been saving for this. By the time you get this letter, I will be dead. Everything is taken care of; I have good comrades, and I have left them very clear instructions.

Be strong, Comrade Daughter, and move on, with my love.

Jack

Rinchen: blog

White with the letter

I drove a long way yesterday with Murray. He was taking me to school but didn't. This is because of the letter. Mum went white with the letter and got up stiff and walked stiff into the study and shut the door. I was scared. She is never stiff she is more like a river. Frozen over now, though, with the letter. Oh Joel, Joel, why can things be bad? And get badder?

Then she came out again with her face covered with crying. I was sick with fear and said nothing. She came up to me like a wonderful swooping bird and held me warm and said oh Rinchen, she said, grandad is dead. And she cried and I didn't cry and said nothing. She is going to Manchester now to be with him though he isn't, and I will go there later to the funeral where he will be burnt while people sing. It is horrible, Joel. And the Chinese shot my mother with an aeroplane and little Fritz was so tiny when he died, trying to hide his little head under the cushion because he wanted his mother but died instead.

Murray drove straight past the school entrance! I was saying nothing, nothing, but when he did that I squeaked. He is very big and very kind and the safest person in the universe and I did feel safe, but stiff. We said the following things:

—No school today. I'm taking you to see someone.

—I don't want to meet a new person today please Murray.

—He is a doctor, he will help you.

—I don't want to go to the doctor please Murray, the smell is dangerous.

—This doctor is different, he is my friend and teacher. I love him.

—Are we going to another school?

—No sweetheart, he teaches healing and fighting, he is Chinese.

—I am frightened of the Chinese Murray.

—You will love him. You are safe with me.

—This is true Murray.

The countryside went by for a long time.

Dr Sun was half the size of Murray but three times as solid. And Murray is the solidest I know. He has a funny high pitched voice and speaks funny English with words missed out and I was scared and then he looked at me straight with black eyes deep, and I felt love, so it was OK. He smiled very very well. And Murray was there like a mountain. So Dr Sun said some strange noises like heeee and haaaa and moved his hands in front of me and suddenly I was shaking. Not little shakes like trembling, but bouncing up and down like on a horse and I felt absolutely out of control and completely safe, it was mad. And I cried. I cried like a hyena. I howled, like an ambulance, for about a month. It was amazing. And then it stopped and I was more calm than I have ever been. I felt empty in the best way. Thank you, thank you, Dr Sun, you are a good Chinese and you smell much safer than normal doctors. And then I slept and dreamed a little and woke up at home on the sofa and Murray was there reading and the sadness came, but it was only sadness.

Hattie, Joel

The funeral

—Joel, I need your support right now.

—You have it. You always have it.

—Murray is taking care of Charlie and Rinchen. Rinchen is taking care of Charlie and Murray. I need you here right by my side.

—And here I am.

—Yes. Yes. I want to sing straight and true. I don't want to cry.

—Yes Comrade.

—Is that you or him?

—Does it matter?

—Oh I adore you—that's just what I needed to hear.

—Yes Comrade.

—OK—I've got it. You can stop saying that now. I'm ready to go. Stay close by my side.

—What are you going to sing?

—Wait and see.

—OK Hattie—my precious treasure—

—Who's that? Joel? Dad? Rinpoche?—don't chuckle like that, I'm trying to concentrate and besides, you're making me want to laugh—they wouldn't understand—it wouldn't be kind.

—Sorry my love—sorry. But stay light. No need for solemnity—just beauty. Here's the moment. You can do it.

—I'm nervous—it's absurd. I mean this is what I do. I'm a singer, for God's sake.

—Remember the skylark.

Hattie, Joel

Charlie's getting up

—Oh Joel—Joel—Charlie's getting up. He's coming to join us. Go and support him—he's very weak.

—He has more strength than you think. You keep on singing. I'll stay right by him in case he needs me. What a class act we are.

—Crazy Wisdom Lady is back. Crazy Wisdom Lady takes Bamford Crem. by storm! Oh Charlie, Charlie, my own dear love. What more could I ask for? Thank you.

Rinchen: blog

Mr Greatheart

I am now going to blog the funeral, because it was the most amazing and wonderful and sad day, awful in bits but the wonderful made up.

We were all there, you see. Charlie came too. Mum said she couldn't leave him. She said she had promised. So we got a wheelchair. It was terrible in my heart to see Charlie in this chair, grey face bony thin, not there at all; Charlie who was the most alive and bouncing person of all. Murray was there to help. Mum was being very strong, as if she was finding all her inside help, as much as she could. It was very hard and I didn't know what to do.

I met a really nice man there called Morris. He was broad and big and Welsh and he was kind to me and explained lots of things, we had a talk. He said grandad was in the International Brigade, in Spain, fighting bad people, which was a wonderful thing; and that Morris's father was also in that, and that's why Morris was there, and he had brought some of his choir. Morris is Welsh. There were all these other big men in tight suits with slightly bashed faces who looked quiet and kind but also danger-ous, Morris said no no don't worry, they're only dangerous to Wallabies, which was a joke. I decided that Morris was a person who was in a book that we read at school, the person is Mr Greatheart.

Mum sang. She sang a song she had written. She just stood there, by the coffin with grandad dead inside it, and put one hand on it, and sang. I stood next to Charlie and I cried and cried, and so did everyone, except Charlie, I can't tell you how beautiful it was, and it was also sad that Charlie was not there to see it, my heart was breaking for that. And then Morris sang a note and then the men began to sing. They sang a song that grandad sang to me once when I was small, the *Internationale*, his eyes got wet and shiny when he did that. Except this time it wasn't like a song. It was like a huge thing that starts very quiet but you still know it's huge, like if lions could sing, much bigger than these big men, big like the sky. And Mum put her voice on top of theirs, high and sweet, it was like electricity. The whole big room with all those people was like we were all in the same electric current, your skin prickled. And I knew that Charlie shouldn't miss this, he just shouldn't, so I said, without think-ing, inside my head, very sharp, Charlie it's time to wake up now. And he did. Oh, he did.

Charlie: journal

Gone to glory

Well, my dears. There I was in the middle of nowhere, between a dream and a dream. And then there was this strange unearthly beautiful roar-ing noise, that made my hair stand on end, in my dream in my nowhere place. And then suddenly sharp like a cutting diamond, a voice, calling me: it's time to wake up now. So of course I did.

And found myself in a wheelchair in a funeral, of all places. Hundreds of people. A Welsh male voice choir, belting out the *Internationale* from the bottom of their collective soul, I've never heard anything like it, God they were good, and Hattie harmonising on top—Hattie! O my love—and so I quite naturally stood up. And everyone turned and looked. Now, my dears, as you know, I am a man of the theatre, so this was irresistible. I started to walk forward, towards Hattie, stumbling a bit, get the suspense in there, pure glory on my face, Welshmen singing like madmen, like big dangerous angels, little Charly two paces behind, careful not to mess up my scene, she's a natural, that child. Hattie opens her arms, tears streaming down her face, singing away, I open my arms, we embrace and kiss. My dears you would have thought the whole congregation had died and gone to glory. And then I thought, oh fuck, I've upstaged the coffin, and then I thought, coffin? God, it must be Hattie's Dad, and a wave of grief and an inexplicable wave of joy flooded through me, but, professional to my fingertips, I hissed at Hattie, *press the button,* and she did, and I held her and she held me and Charly scrunged between us and we all watched Jack start to move towards the flames. And someone, Murray for sure, God bless him, started to clap, and they all started, clapping and whooping and whistling, the choir still singing, louder and louder, such an outburst of collective joy I have never experienced in all of my life. And, over all of it, rising and rising, Hattie's laughter, her gladness healing my heart.

Hattie

Is this really you?

—Well—that went well. I hope I did things the way you wanted them done.

—Perfect, Comrade Daughter.

—What did you like best?

—Do you really want to know?

—Of course I do.

—I liked it that you sang.

—And the song?

—Yes dear child of my heart—I loved the song. Thank you for writing it.

—OK—now hold on a minute. Is this really you?

—Why do you doubt it?

—Because 'dear child of my heart' is the sort of thing I say. I've never heard you say it before.

—But I wasn't dead before.

—Does it make that much difference?

—You'd be surprised. It's not as different as I'd supposed.

—Am I just making this up? Is this some clever trick of my mind?

—How does it feel?

—It feels great. I suppose that's why I'm doubting it. Textbook case of denial, don't you think?

Rinchen: blog

A quiet man

It is different now. Charlie is with us all the time, he is now a quiet man. He has an inside look on his face. He will see me seeing him and smile, and then be inside again. He eats, but not very much, and doesn't drink wine or fool around at all. He is still thin. There is a strong feel to him, there is a definite thing that he is doing. Strong and keen and thin, like a knife. It is mostly inside.

When we eat together it is very quiet. This is nice. Mum watches him, like a mother keeping an eye on a child, she is caring. They sit together by the window, not talking. They are happy together in this silence, which makes me cry in a nice way.

And what else he does is write. Writing and writing, patter patter on his beautiful little white laptop. So much writing, you can see it, what the it is I don't know, flowing down his arms through his fingers into the little white computer. I do hope he is backing it up like I showed him.

So we are in a peaceful time together, and I can feel that things are taking shape and happening, shaping, growing, and there is no more danger at the moment.

May 2004

Hattie: letter

Your marvellous choir

Dear Morris,

I'm writing to thank you for being there at Dad's funeral. Please thank your marvellous choir too. The sound they produced was absolutely magnificent—and so warm and heartfelt, as well as skilful. I know that Lawrence has paid for your expenses (Dad left such clear instructions about everything) but I hope you'll be easy in accepting this personal gift from me as a donation towards your ongoing musical work. I hope it'll be useful.

I do have another reason for writing. I'm trying to remember something from an afternoon when I was quite a young child. Your father came to visit us in the little house in Dove Street. So it must have been in the late fifties. I can remember that he and Dad were reminiscing about something and I know that he was tremendously excited later that evening and talked to Mum about it, and she was moved to tears by his words. Do you happen to have any more information about what it was?

My love and thanks to you—and my good wishes to Margaret please.

Hattie Tattersall.

Morris: letter

Thank you

Hello Hattie,

Thank you for your letter. And for the very generous donation to the choir.

Smashing. It will help us prepare for our trip to Mannheim next year. The lads and I were really proud to sing at your Dad's funeral. And they haven't stopped talking about your voice. I'd warned them. 'Now then, Lads,' I said at our rehearsal in the coach on the way up to Bamford, 'Now then, we're going to sing with an angel—you'd better give it everything you've got, because it's the nearest you bloody lot are ever going to get to an angel.' Pete Pritchard, on the way home, was in tears when he talked about you. 'Bloody right Morris,' he said, 'if that's what it sounds like in heaven, I'd better mend my ways'. Mind you, he was several pints down by that stage—and still going strong. It'd take a lot for Pete to mend his ways. Still, he's a grand tenor, and he puts his all into the music—which is all I ask for really.

Now, I've given some thought to your question, and I can't say that I know the answer. But I'm seeing my father on Saturday and will ask him and get back to you.

Take good care of yourself now. You gave your Dad a good send-off.

Margaret sends her love.

Morris

Rinchen: blog

Strange now

Everything is strange now. Wintry. Strange. I am strange too.

Charlie is not like Charlie. He is a strange kind searching man, very quiet, sitting, thinking, writing, dreaming. The house is quiet around him. The cat sits with him a lot. I sit with him too. It is the opposite of Charlie. Except for the kind.

Mum is strange and purified. Grandad is dead. Murray is quiet, and sits, and practices his fighting things a lot. He is looking after us like an invisible shield. Joel is quiet too; he also is part of the shield. And inside this we are working, working.

I go to school but it is not the same. I am learning yes but learning different now. It is Tibetan learning I think. I have a Tibetan feeling inside. I can go inside that feeling and hang out there and it is very cool, also warm.

And, this is a secret, blog, Rinpoche comes now when I dream. Mostly I can't remember or it is only strange memory but he is building somehow the Tibetan place inside me. The Tibetan place is like being in a high snow valley, so high and pure, the sky as blue as if you were seeing blue for the first time ever, blue, blue. And warm because the warm is inside, or you are inside a safe bubble of warmth.

What is happening to us, Joel? Joel?

Joel is very quiet. I think it is good, what is happening, but it is strange.

Charlie: journal

Falling off the roundabout

—Hello? Hello? Who's calling? Charlie, is that you? It's your number. Is your phone working?

—Charlie, are you OK?

It was very strange. I couldn't say anything. I'd managed to switch the phone on, hit the right speed dial number, and then just stood there, with my mouth open, nothing coming out. My head full of thoughts, burning with, teeming with thoughts, and nothing coming out. Eventually, I managed:

—Merry … go … round.

—Charlie! What's the matter with you? Where are you?

My voice was a soft croak. I was a heavy breather. Oh, Hattie, I must have sounded awful.

What I wanted to tell her was, there was a merry-go-round, when I was six years old. Animals, smooth golden animals, lion and unicorn and lord knows what, with this uniform rictus grin on their horrible unreal faces, up and down, round and round, I was terrified. So I tried to get off, and fell off, and broke my little six year old arm. The sudden outrageous pain. The pain was impossible, inconceivable, and yet there it was, and on it went, and I screamed and screamed.

I wanted to tell her, Hattie, Hattie, I've fallen off the merry-go-round again.

Well. Good in a crisis, is our Hattie. She called my PA. Who said I was at the theatre, doing a charity gig for a bunch of sick kids. So she called the theatre, and they told her what had happened.

There were so many of them, you see; so many. And every single one of them was very sick, and some of them were really horribly disabled. They used not to exist, you know, the really bad ones. They never had a chance to exist, because the doctors would simply take an executive decision at birth and they wouldn't survive. Now the doctors won't do that any more, and who can blame them (either way, dear God, who can blame them) and so all these children, *children* for God's sake, with a quality of life that is frankly obscene, it is unacceptable, it is utterly utterly not to be countenanced, and there they are. There is no God. And there they are. And there I am, in a fucking clown suit, do you begin to see my existential dilemma? Going round and round, up and down, with a rictus grin, and I couldn't do it any more. Not any more at all no way. So I corpsed. I dried. I stood there with my mouth open and nothing came out. And that was worse, much worse, because they had been laughing, and now they stopped. And I broke every rule, every single rule that has held me together in the whole of my life as an actor, the most basic theatre survival rule that I have, which is, don't walk away; and I walked away.

God knows how she did it. She picked up Murray and drove like a demented angel and got to central London in an impossible time and—how did she know to bring Murray?—cut through the mob outside the dressing room door, which I had managed to lock, and Murray kicked the door in, scarcely breaking step, they said, and they found me on the floor, crying into a dead phone. He picked me up, Jesus he's strong, and we were out and in the car, me in the back in Hattie's arms, Murray driving, off back to Henley.

Charlie: journal

Fugue

Fugue. That's what they call it. After the first time, I read some books. Fugue. I was a fugitive. I was flying, fleeing, failing, falling. Fly the friendly skies with Icarus airlines. They put me to bed in that big comfortable house, that welcoming place, and there I stayed. Out of it. Oh, not unconscious, as such, everything worked, they said, Charlie the robot, fully functional, nothing inside. Didn't say a word. Didn't eat. Drank a little.

Peed occasionally. That was about it—outside. Inside, inside, there was a whole lot of shaking going on.

Charlie: journal

There I lay

So there I was, my dears, there I lay. It was strange, though it didn't feel it, it just felt, this is how things are. Slow, is how things were. Infinitely slow. I was an old old man. Creaking, everything took such effort. My thoughts slowed too; the conscious self, the driver of the machine, was swamped by the job, was definitely doing the minimum. Eating, for instance: out of the question. Too complicated. Biting, chewing, swallowing, no, wait, you have to get the stuff to your mouth first, choose the chunk you're going to eat next—dear God, choosing! Out of the question. My mouth got very dry, often, and they gave me liquid, and somehow I managed to process it, in at one end, out the other, not sure how. 'They' was also rather problematic. There were people—were they people? It's hard to say. There were dreams. Day and night were the same. Someone there was who radiated heat, like a furnace. A hot goodness. There was singing. Hattie's voice, talking, talking, I don't know what she said. An old man, sometimes, purring; and the room would fill with rainbows. A man in a black robe, who was Joel.

I was content, to be in that between state. There was a lot of greyness, the unformed was everywhere, no focus, but there was nothing to choose, either, or display, or ward off, or be.

So I dreamed. But they were movie dreams, I wasn't in them. I watched, though that's too strong a word; they flowed round me. They were.

Charlie: journal

Shakespeare on my mind

It starts at the fingertips. Life, seeping back: a glow, a warmth, a sense of possibility.

—You look a lot better today, Charlie.

—Do I, sweetheart?

—Bits of you look like Charlie again.

Ah. I didn't ask, which bits?

So what can I use this experience for, I ask myself? The statuesque Hermione in *Winter's Tale*? One of those living statue street theatre roles? Not really my style, my loves. Not quite my cup of tea.

The poet Donne, in his shroud? The Bard himself, in his Stratford death statue? Which always looked to me, every time I did the pilgrimage, which, my loves, was many times, like one of those old coin-in-the-slot gadgets: you pop in a penny, well, let's say a pound, nowadays, the quill goes scratch scratch scratch, and out comes—a sonnet! Shall I compare, insert name here, to a summer's day?

—Charlie! You're smiling!

—No I'm not.

—You are, you are! Charlie, stop pulling horrible faces! I saw you smile!

And, indeed, I did. I smiled.

Shakespeare. I got Shakespeare on my mind. The bald Bard, with the bulging brow. Or the furtive unshaven poacher of the other portrait, what's it called? Indeed you are, old fox; you are the prince of poachers, out there in the night thickets of literature, looking for plots to steal.

—What are you thinking about, Charlie?

—Shakespeare, my love.

—He was the best, wasn't he, Charlie?

—The best what, precious?

—I don't know. What did he do?

Well, yes, what did he do? Tell me, master, teacher, sweet poet, emperor of the unspeakable, what was it, again, that you did? Something to do with plays, was it?

—Plays, my love, he wrote plays and poems.

—What for, Charlie? What were they for?

Rinchen, Charlie

Rinchen's poem

—Do you want to hear my poem Charlie?

—I would simply adore to hear your poem, darling girl. Wait a moment while I put my listening to a poem whilst the poet is present face on.

—What sort of face is that?

—What does it look like?

—It looks like a going to church when you don't really want to and pretending to think the sermon's interesting face.

—When have you been to church and sat through a sermon, O child of the magical mystery tour?

—With my friend Annabel Atkinson of course. Are you going to listen to my poem or not?

—Am. Definitely. Am going to.

—Well put on another face then please.

—Any particular kind of face?

—Yes—the old face. The face before you were ill face please.

—I don't think I know how to do that face anymore, sweetheart.

—That's just silly. Please, Charlie. We need you to be better now.

—We?

—Me and Mum and Joel. We.

—Rinchen, please don't cry. Please don't cry. I am better. I am. Just different, that's all. Read me your poem. Please.

Rinchen, Charlie

Poem

Let me show you the following cat,
of such grace and such purity that,
when the great and the good
need to be understood,
or the halt and the lame
need a touch of the same,

or the beautiful young
need their song to be sung,
or the weary and grey
need to brighten their day,
or the lonely and sad
need a chance to be glad,
then this cat will awake with the wink of an eye
and a yawn and a stretch and compassionate sigh
and the happiness grows
as he uncurls his toes
and the brush of his paw
leaves them laughing for more
and the ease of his dance
brings them out of their trance
and the grace of his gaze
makes them grateful for days
and the shine of his fur
makes them gurgle and purr
with a love that's intense
as they get a real sense
of the following cat
who will make them see that
the secret of life is in wisdom and kindness
and that, he will tell them, is that.

If you think that this song
might go on for too long,
if you think this not tender and true,
then we must recommend
when you come to the end
our cat who is waiting for you.
Just you.
Our cat who is waiting for you.

—That's my poem Charlie. Do you like it?

—I simply adore it, darling girl.

—It's for you Charlie. I wrote it for you.

Charlie, Rinchen

Because they're not real

—Rinchen, dearest, would you like to go for a walk?

—A walk? Out of the house? You haven't been out of the house since you went into retreat.

—Since I what?

—You know, went inside yourself to check things out.

—Is that what I did?

—Of course it is, Charlie, don't be silly. Now come on, we'll go down to the pool and look at the badger hole.

—A bit cold and wet, isn't it, my love?

—Charlie it is a wonderful day because you are going for a walk in it, I am so happy.

—Hmm. You are happy a lot, aren't you, dear.

—Mostly, sort of, yes. It's very important to be happy, Charlie. Because when you are smiling, the whole world smiles with you. I read that in a book.

—Hmm. Listen, Rinchen, you watch TV, go to movies, go to watch plays, don't you?

—Of course Charlie, you know that, we've done stuff together like that.

—Right. Why?

—Well, because they're not real, of course.

—What do you mean?

—Well, obviously, because you get a bit scared or a bit sad in a pretend way like a dream, and then it's over and the feeling stops and empties itself, and you are happy to realise it wasn't real, it was just a dream or a movie or something.

—The cloud capped towers, the gorgeous palaces / Are like this insubstantial pageant faded / And leave not a rack behind.

—You do say clever things sometimes, Charlie.

—That was Shakespeare, dearest.

—Ah. The best.

—Yes.

—But you don't want to dream too much, Charlie, because otherwise you might think the dream is real. If you thought the theatre was real life you would be a sad person.

—As opposed to happy.

—You got it, Charlie.

—I'm getting it. I think. My love.

Hattie, Charlie

Mornington Crescent

—Hey Charlie what are you doing?

—Contemplating my navel, dear heart. It is full of lint.

—You could try contemplating your heart instead.

—The foul rag and bone shop?

—Or?

—Else?

—In awe? Elsinore? Mornington Crescent, I think.

—A hit. A palpable hit. Did they have underground trains in Elsinore?

—I'm sorry I haven't a clue.

—I could never put one past you, could I, dear heart.

—Why would you want to?

—I'm a song and dance man. I run as fast as I can, so that I can't be caught.

—And the song is?

—It depends on the audience, and the director, and the show. My business is show business my love.

—OK. I'm the audience. You're the director. What's the song?

—Make 'em laugh. Make them laugh. Nobody wants to cry.

—How is Nobody today?

—Touché, sunshine. Nobody is doing just fine.

June 2004

Morris: letter

Ask her to come here

Dear Hattie,

Just a note to say I spoke to my Father about the conversation with your Dad, and he went very quiet, looking into the far off distance and dead serious. Most unlike himself, actually, I was quite perturbed for a while there. Anyway, he came to after a long silence and said 'You'd better ask her to come here Morris. I need to tell her face to face.' I tried to get him to say more but he stayed serious and put out a hand to stop me. 'My lips are sealed Morris. Don't ask'. Didn't matter what I did after that—he wouldn't say anything more about it.

So you'd better come and see us, my love. I can take you in the car to the place where he lives now. It's only five miles away. Margaret says you're most welcome to stop the night here, if you'd like to.

So give us a call and let us know what suits you.

Cheers

Morris

Hattie: journal

Owen and Jack

Owen is frail, but very upright. Morris told me in the car that he has very limited vision now, but his eyes are the same piercing blue lights I remember from my childhood. He looks directly at you when he speaks, and turns his head to the left and down a little when he listens. I'd forgotten that movement of the head—like a shy, sensitive animal, deferring to the impact of noise. I took his hand in mine and held it. It seemed the right thing to do.

—I'm glad to see you, Hattie, he said.

—I'm very glad to be here.

Morris had told him all about the funeral, and he said again how sad he was not to have been there. He looked down at his trembling legs and shrugged. More a gesture of acceptance than frustration. I remember him as feisty. Vehement. An orator, holding forth with passionate inflections, even in the small kitchen in Dove Street.

He wanted to know about my life. About Rinchen. About the songs. I asked him about all those the years when we'd not been in touch—but he waved his hand, dismissing ghosts, and said he preferred not to live in the past.

We sat in the garden for a while. It's a pretty place. Well cared for and sensitively laid out—different private places for visitors to sit comfortably with the residents. Morris was enthusiastic about the new piece he's rehearsing with the choir and made Owen laugh—me too. They asked me to sing—right there in the garden—so I did. Just improvising around some old Irish tunes. And Morris joined in and let his graceful, delicate hands curve in certain flight through the air around him. Such a big solid man. Such gentle, sensitive hands.

When it was nearly time for us to go, Owen asked Morris to leave us alone together for a few minutes. In the silence that followed I was surprised to find that my heart was suddenly beating very fast. Was it fear? Surely not. Surely not.

It was several days before I could bring myself even to look properly at the envelope and the box that Owen had given me. The envelope with its dear, familiar writing. There was something about the slight tremor in his hands as he passed it to me that told me there was something here that was quite other, startling and new.

—I'm not going to talk about it—not going to talk about it, he said. Let's just say, your Dad and me—we had an understanding. When we came back to England, we talked about it just that once in Dove street—that time that you can remember. He said he would tell your mam about it.

I agreed to that. It was right that he should. But after that we knew we would keep silent unless someone asked. He gave me this box to keep for you. There's a letter in it, I think. He knew you would ask for it eventually. You've asked Hattie. So here's everything you need: the box, and this new envelope. Your Dad sent me this new one in April, when he was setting his affairs in order. Said to tell you to read it before the one in the box.

And with that he told me to call Morris back so that we could say our goodbyes. He returned to his usual jaunty manner and assumed an authoritative tone of voice. And we did say goodbye—with love, but with respectful boundaries in place.

—Thank you for the singing, Hattie. Thank you for the singing Morris, he said—looking straight into our faces. He took our hands once more—patted me gently on the arm, turned, and walked slowly back into the house.

It was the last time we met. He died two days later. Peaceably, and asleep in the garden.

Hattie, Morris

I don't know

—What do you think it is, Morris?

—Well, I dunno, love. Looks like quite a fancy box to me—didn't know my Dad kept such things. He's always been very strict about clutter. Never liked things that were just ornaments—very puritanical that way. Are you going to open it?

—I don't know, Morris. I really don't know.

Hattie, Charlie

Thinking about my sins

—Hey Charlie

—Hattie. Hi.

—What are you doing?

—Thinking about my sins.

—Is that interesting?

—I wish they were more interesting, I have been a tedious sinner, my love.

—Yes, if you're going to sin, whatever that means, you might as well make it interesting. Anything you want to share with me?

—Doubt is a sin. Or so I was taught at school. Despair is a sin, so they said. Anomie, soul-destruction, that's a sin.

—Well, Charlie, doubt comes and goes. Despair comes and comes. Bleak boredom comes and goes. But awareness of these things is constant. If you could pay attention to the awareness you would see that these sins of yours are just flotsam and jetsam.

—The trouble is my love that the flotsam, and indeed the jetsam, is what I am hanging on to, to stop myself drowning, sorry if that sounds melo-dramatic.

—More dramatic than mellow sweetheart. I do have a suggestion. Do you want to hear it?

—Yes. Please.

—OK, right here, right now, let yourself drown, and see what happens.

—The waters close. Light fails. Blackness. End of story.

—Not end of story. Keep on drowning. See what happens.

—Suffocation. A sweeping in of sensation flooding to terminate. Black-ness gets blacker.

—Charlie, trust me. Go straight into the blackness.

—I trust you, I don't trust me.

—I understand that. Go into the blackness.

—Oo. Oo.

—Say more.

—It's quite nice. It's not unbearable.

—Stay with the experience. Keep meeting it. Keep going forwards. And when you can, tell me what it's like.

—Well, it's odd. It's a coming out the other side sort of feeling. It's, I don't know, it's, erm, like swimming in milky cloud. Confusing. No direction. No direction at all.

Charlie: journal

The dog's tooth

So there was a well, a fountain of writing in me, and maybe not much else. So much of me that had been me was gone. No jokes, my dears, no more laughs, no voices, pratfalls, mockery, no faces to put on. No more masks, because no face to put the mask on to. Nobody. Very peaceful, it was, in an empty sort of way.

Charly would come and sit with me. Rinchen, I think she is now; I think she is coming into a self, as I am exiting from one. She is becoming quite strange, actually, strangely beautiful, interior, there is a kind of growing certainty about her, a sense of smiling. It is, really, very nice.

Hattie, too, my dearest Hattie, is looking better now. When I first came back from wherever I was, she was gaunt, stretched, tenuous. I had never seen her like that: for me, she was always the power in my life, the assurance: knowing that someone like that was possible made anything possible and everything OK. Which, of course, it's not.

And now, for me, rebuilding. And the writing, which is pouring forth. And for her? She is on a quest, I think; this is wonderful, I know her quests, they are a sign she is alive. Is herself again.

And—

—Hello, Rinchen. I think you are Rinchen now, aren't you?

—Yes, Charlie.

—Why is that, then?

—Because you are working out who Charlie is, and I don't want to confuse you.

—Ah. Sensible.

—Yes.

—Tell me a story, Rinchen; I want to be full of stories, full and overfull.

—OK. This is a Tibetan story, that Simon told me. Once there was a young man who travelled to India, and his mother, who was very religious, asked him, begged him, before he went, to bring her back a Buddha relic from India. But he forgot. He only remembered when he was coming back into the valley where the village of his mother was.

"What shall I do?" he wondered. And then he saw a dead dog by the side of the road. So he pulled out a tooth from the dog's skull, wrapped it in fine gold cloth, and gave it to his mother: here is a tooth of the Lord Buddha, he said.

And then he left, to travel again, leaving his mother very happy.

A year later he came back. The valley was full of pilgrims, and miracles; the sick were cured, the lame walked, the whole valley was full of holiness, you could feel it, like a bowl of warm water. His mother's devotion was so strong that she changed the dog's tooth into a Buddha tooth. The end.

—Thank you, Rinchen.

—Thank you for listening, Charlie.

Charlie: journal

Mispronunciation

This little white machine is my friend and confidant. It sits there like an open book, and out comes all this strange stuff from inside me. No, dears, not my early childhood nightmares, though there were a good sprinkling of those; no. Medieval dreams. Just let it flow, let it flow, my dear Charlot; and see what it turns into.

That story, the dog's tooth, sits in my mind. It seems so obvious, what it's about: religion is a fake. Cynical son plays cruel joke on aged and devout mother. Fake tooth (actually, disgusting fake tooth—aren't dogs the lowest of the low in the East?) becomes centre of fake cult and obligingly produces its share of no doubt fake miracles; because how can a dog's tooth be as potent as a tooth of the Buddha? Right, clear enough. So how on earth is that a Buddhist teaching story? Why did Simon tell it to Rinchen? What is going on?

Later.

—Hello dear.

—Hello Charlie.

—The story of the dog's tooth, what's it about?

—Pardon?

—What does it mean?

—I told you, Charlie, it means that a man was going to India and he promised his mother—

—Hm. OK. It means what it says?

—Of course, what else would it mean?

—But the mother was tricked, she thought a dog's tooth was the Buddha's tooth. And so were all the pilgrims tricked, weren't they?

—Yes, Charlie.

—Well isn't that a bad thing?

—I don't know Charlie, I wasn't there.

—Hm. Hm. Rinchen, do you know any more stories like that?

—Yes, Charlie. Would you like me to tell you another story?

—Yes, dear.

—Once upon a time there was an old man who had lived in retreat by himself in a cave most of his life. And Rinpoche, when he was young, went to visit him, because he had heard that this man was very wise and very holy, and in Tibet when you hear about someone like that you go to see them and hope they will give you teachings. So he did. Rinpoche had been doing a lot of studying, studying, and wanted always to know more.

So he came to the cave and there was the old man and he looked very strange and wild and wise and weird. And they had a conversation which I didn't understand. And then they were quiet and the old man began to hum a mantra. A mantra is like a magic spell. This mantra was a big secret mantra very important, and Rinpoche knew it because he had received an initiation from a very high lama. And the problem was, the old man was saying it wrong. It's very bad to say a mantra wrong because you can cause harm and all sorts. So Rinpoche felt he had to tell the old man, and he did, very respectfully. So the old man said 'ho', just like that. 'Ho', again. 'Wrong sound yes?' He said. Then he took out his *purba* which is a big knife and Rinpoche was a little nervous and the old man said the mantra in the true proper way and struck the knife at a big rock. And it went 'pang' and nothing happened. Then he said the mantra in his way and struck the rock with his purba and the knife went into the rock zip all the length of the blade. And they both looked at it for a bit. And the old man said 'I think my way of saying it is better'. And Rinpoche bowed and asked for a blessing. The end.

Charlie: journal

Why do you do what you do?

—Charlie, answer me, why is it that you do what you do?

—What do you mean, Rinchen?

—Your plays, your Shakespeare, your clowning, your singing and dancing, all that wonderful thing that you do. Why do you do it?

Humph. I was taken aback. I did not have an answer.

—Why do you ask, dear?

—Because Rinpoche says, you must ask, always ask. He says you must push where it hurts. It is always important to find out. That is what he says. Hurting, healing, same place. Check, he says; check it out. Not believe, check. That's what he says. He doesn't say all the words, like Tibetan. Tibetan is quite strange, Charlie, it doesn't waste time.

—When did he say all this to you, beloved?

—From time to time. From. Time. To. Time. That's when.

OK, I can't handle this. I know what I know. I am Charlie Beaumont, actor, writer, impresario, clown. Clown. That's who I am. The song and dance man. I know how to make an audience laugh, cry, jump out of their seats, I can give them a very nice time. I can take them out of themselves, myself out of myself; I can do that. That's it. That's all. That's enough. Isn't it?

Isn't it, old mole, old duke of darkness, Shakespeare my contemporary, is that not it? Tell me, tell me, enigmatic statue, is that not enough? Make them laugh, make them cry, make them fall out of the everyday, give them a good time, put the bums on the seats, that's it, right, Bard of my heart, devious bastard, that's it and only all the it there is, right? Right?

That moment: vaudeville satori. That's it, right, when you can believe that a man can fly?

There is, there is, no more than that. That, dear Rinchen, dear Charlie, is what it is for. That, beloved, is all she wrote.

Charlie: journal

Shakespeare's worth

OK, William, my heart in hiding, supreme poet of the South Midlands, time for a showdown. What is it actually worth, a life devoted to you and your subtle art?

What do you believe? No-one knows, no-one has the slightest idea. What is your point, your message, your package to live by? Nobody has the least notion.

Right, *nul points* to Stratford on the message front; what's left? Why, words and people, Charlie, what else? Such words, such characters, what more do you want? *The Communist Manifesto?* Oh, and entrancement, don't forget that. The rough magic. And, not forgetting, depth. Such depth, such resonance, vistas without limit.

OK, that sounds pretty good. Take them one by one. Check, ask, investigate, says my little disconcerting friend.

Depth. Well, yes. There are a lot of books. Full marks for services to the Shakespeare industry. On the other hand, I do have to say, as a man of the theatre, my dears, I do have to offer the considered opinion, fuck that for a game of soldiers. Anyone can find anything they want in Shakespeare, and does. Hamlet was not written to satisfy Polonius, the unbelievably stupid and inventive interpreter. The rat in the arras.

No. No. Entrancement? OK, that's nice, people must be amused, and if feeling exalted amuses them, even better. But is that it? Is that all?

Oh, the parts. Such fantastic parts. So unexpected, various, so deconstructive, disrespectful, dirt and diamonds, the laughter of the heart. And the lines: you walk on stage, and he hands you a trumpet. Here you are son, he says, blow down that and if you know your stuff you'll knock their socks off. And, by God, if you do, you do. Every single time, whether you are Hamlet or Second Murderer.

Entrancement. The rough magic. The subtle art.

Rinchen, Charlie

Calling Joel

—Charlie . . .

—Hello, precious.

—I have a question for you . . .

—Go ahead, sweetheart.

—Why don't you call Joel?

—That's a good question.

—What's the answer?

—I have to think about that, Rinchen.

—What's to think about?

—Is that you or him speaking like that?

—Me, I think—why?—does it sound like him?

—Just like. Just like.

—Don't cry, Charlie. No need to cry. Come and eat something. I've made something so special you won't believe.

Rinchen, Joel

Coming to the West

—Rinpoche said it was very important, that I should come to the West, but he hasn't told me why. He hasn't told anyone why. But that's why he carried me, all that long way. Do you know why, Joel?

—Yes dear.

—Are you going to tell me?

—No dear, not yet.

—OK then.

Charlie, Hattie

Talking with Joel

—Hattie. Does Rinchen talk with Joel?

—Yes, she does.

—How long has she been doing that?

—Several years, I think. I can't remember whether she called him or he called her. I suppose she would have called him. But maybe not.

—And you're OK with that?

—Yes of course. It's good for her. Can you pass me those tomatoes—I want them for the salad.

—And for him? Is it good for him?

—Oh yes. Oh yes. Of course. And the olive oil now?

—This one?

—No, the little bottle please.

—Do you think it would be good for Joel if I called too?

—Yes. I do. Have you seen the parmesan?

Charlie: journal

Ready to write

OK, Joel. I know you're waiting for me to get in touch. I'm not ready to speak with you yet, but I am ready to write something. What? I'm not sure. Some more film script? Yes. A scene or two from the early days. The happy days. Keep it light, Charlot. Keep it safe. Yes, here I am keeping it safe. Forgive me dear old friend. Forgive my cowardice. This is the best I can do.

Charlie: filmscript 27

Church gig

INT. CHARLIE'S HOUSE: KITCHEN—AFTERNOON

SPRING 1971

JOEL
What about finals?

HATTIE
Finals? Finals?

JOEL

Yes. Remember? Those big exams we're supposed to be preparing for? The wall charts, the lists, the deadlines?

HATTIE

Well, we're just about ready. As ready as we'll ever be. We know what we know. The break will do us good.

CHARLIE

She's right. Besides, we have panache.

JOEL

You and Cyrano de Bergerac have panache. I have hard work and study.

HATTIE

Oh come on, Joel—you've studied all your life. You can charm the socks off any examiner. This is our first real gig. Paid. Posters.

CHARLIE

And it's going to please my Grandfather. It's a family thing.

JOEL

Is that supposed to win me over? I'm a bit off family things, actually. Doing my level best to avoid them.

HATTIE

Well, if something were to win you over what would it be?

JOEL

It would have to be in a good cause. Something really worthwhile.

CHARLIE

Right. I'll ring the Vicar straight away. He must have dozens of good causes up his surplice sleeve

Cut to scenes of HATTIE *and* JOEL *and* CHARLIE *packing instruments into van. No special sound equipment—they're primarily acoustic at this point.*

Then scenes from inside van—rolling along English countryside in late May. Cotswold territory. HATTIE *and* CHARLIE *in front seats, reading maps, getting lost, going down little tracks that lead nowhere and having to back the van up etc.* JOEL *sitting in back of van, deep in a book and making notes. Eventually they turn up at a small idyllic country village. English pastoral. There's a fête on the green; flags, bunting, stalls, the usual paraphernalia. They park by a little, beautiful church.* HATTIE *and* CHARLIE *get down from the van.* JOEL *stays inside, still lost in the book.*

HATTIE

My God it's the 1950's, did you take a wrong turn?

A VOICE FROM BEHIND CAMERA

A lot to be said for the 1950's.

CHARLIE

Ah. Hattie—meet my Grandfather.

ANOTHER VOICE FROM BEHIND CAMERA

A lot to be said for God.

CHARLIE

And Father John. Vicar of this parish.

HATTIE laughs her laugh. Unstoppable laughter. CHARLIE and the two men have to join in—what appeared to be a sticky moment dissolves in bonhomie.

JOEL arrives—book in hand—troubled expression on his face—to see what's going on.

VICAR

(Extends his hand to HATTIE) Your laughter is like the laughter of God.

JOEL

(Hearing the quotation from Rumi, he throws his book in the air—suddenly carefree) OK. Where's the gig?

Shots of the band setting up. An elegant venue. A drawing room. It is in CHARLIE'S GRANDFATHER's stately home. Late afternoon. There is a baby grand with good sound. We see them as they watch the audience arrive— an assortment of English village people—all ages. The chairs are arranged formally. The two centre chairs in the front row have 'reserved' notices on them. When the room is full, CHARLIE'S GRANDFATHER and the VICAR arrive and take the reserved seats.

HATTIE and JOEL and CHARLIE look at each other and pull faces. They have no idea what might please this audience.

HATTIE

Leave it to me. I'll lead. You follow. We'll give them 'Taking the Slow Train'.

They take their places. A little abashed. A little hesitant. Then HATTIE begins to play and sing. Her voice astonishes the audience. They are immediately

entranced. GRANDFATHER *and* VICAR *break into broad, encouraging smiles.*
JOEL *and* CHARLIE *join in. Everyone is happy.*

I'm taking the slow train
it's crowded with angels
I'm going on the slow train—yes the slow train
where the air is sweet with love
I'm going on the slow train
crowded with angels
I'm on the slow train—so many angels
and we are learning—yes we are learning
about love

the woman right beside me
is an old close friend of Jesus
we talk of late night shopping
and the need for love
the young man by the window
is a look alike for Gabriel
he holds a bunch of lilies
that he's picked with love

I'm going on the slow train
crowded with angels
I'm on the slow train—so many angels
and we are learning—yes we are learning
about love

the arrival of the trolley
brings a sandwich filled with kindness
a biscuit with beatitude
and tea with love
the newly opened window
blows a wind of change right through me
and the rain across the landscape
hails a storm of love

I'm going on the slow train
crowded with angels
I'm on the slow train—so many angels
and we are learning—yes we are learning

about love

the wheels are strumming
the carriage sings
the tracks are humming
this train has wings
Archangel Michael has a megaphone
he tells the guards van
we're happy, and we're

taking the slow train
taking the slow train
taking the slow train
home

Later that evening.

HATTIE and CHARLIE are sitting with GRANDFATHER at a dining room table. Remains of a meal are on the table. Wine still being drunk. A sense of friendly decorum. Pleasant conversation. Mellow, not intense.

Cut to

JOEL and VICAR sitting astride chairs in the empty drawing room—amidst the scattered debris of the aftermath of the concert. They have plates of food on the floor beside them—largely untouched—wine glasses to hand from which they take an occasional swig. They are deep in philosophical debate. Completely engaged. Happy and spirited and excited. A sense of cut and thrust, but basic accord.

Enter HATTIE

HATTIE

I hate to interrupt but we need to be going now. 1500-1640 tomorrow.

VICAR

Fifteen hundred? Three o'clock?

HATTIE

Sadly, no. English Literature period paper. Finals.

VICAR

My dear. You came all this way and gave us all this time when you have a Finals paper tomorrow? What can I say? *(Turns to JOEL)* You too?

JOEL

Yes. We're all starting a run of exams tomorrow—roughly two a day for a week and a half. Excepting Sunday of course.

VICAR

And Saturday?

JOEL

No. The Registry doesn't recognise minority faiths. Fortunately I didn't take the Bibliography and Palaeography option, which falls on Saturday.

VICAR

So no dilemma there then?

JOEL

No.

They exchange broad smiles and slap each other on the back. They have had a wonderful time together.

We see HATTIE and CHARLIE in the van, waiting to go. JOEL and the VICAR are still talking nineteen to the dozen and waving their arms around in debate.

HATTIE

Joel! Jo-el!

JOEL and VICAR walk to front of van. JOEL climbs into front seat next to CHARLIE.

VICAR

Come back soon. Come to the Vicarage. I've got some 12th century texts to show you.

JOEL

I will, John. Thank you. Thanks.

VICAR

And thanks to all of you. Wonderful music. You deserve to go far.

They drive off—waving and cheery. JOEL sinks back into seat and closes his eyes. He is satisfied but tired.

HATTIE

So what on earth were you two talking about?

JOEL

Kabbalah. That man knows Kabbalah.

HATTIE

You're kidding. What's he doing being a parish Vicar in the middle of the Cotswolds?

JOEL

Time. It gives him time. To study.

HATTIE

But how does he reconcile the mysticism with the regular duties of the parish? What about the liturgy? How does he manage?

JOEL

Dilemmas. Exquisite moral dilemmas. Every day, thank God. Every day.

CHARLIE

So you're not alone then?

JOEL

Exactly. Thank you so much for persuading me to do this. I feel reassured. So comforted.

HATTIE

We're really pleased for you, Joel.

CHARLIE

And we did a good job.

JOEL

They loved us. They really loved us.

They drive along through the darkness in companionable silence. HATTIE is driving. JOEL appears to doze.

After a while, he sits bolt upright and turns to CHARLIE.

JOEL

What was the good cause by the way?

CHARLIE

(Keeping a straight face though HATTIE is smiling) Don't ask, Sunshine. Just don't ask.

JOEL relaxes back. HATTIE starts suppressed laughter and then lets it rip. The others laugh too. We see (but JOEL doesn't) outside the car window posters

for a benefit performance in aid of a local rare-breed pig farmer.
A song, 'Your laughter is like the laughter of God,' plays over shots of van driving off into the night.

epiphany tuesday—prism offered in dew
wild rose in the pine woods—the fullness of blue
envelop me under and over and through
in your laugh
in your laughter
in you.

necklace of jasmine—a heron that flew
cicadas in pine woods—the goodness of blue
envelop me under and over and through
in your laugh
in your laughter
in you

envelop the antelope—laughter of God
circle the cantaloupe—laughter of God
spiral the espadrille—laughter of God
umbrella the slumberer—laughter of God
envelop me under and over and through
in your laugh
in your laughter
in you

embrace the rememberer—laughter of God
hold all the beholders—laughter of God
encompass the magnet—laughter of God
camouflage the mirage—laughter of God
envelop me under and over and through
in your laugh
in your laughter
in you

revolve the voluminous—laughter of God
whirl with the dervishes—laughter of God
display the aurora—laughter of God
mellow the cello—laughter of God

envelop me under and over and through
in your laugh
in your laughter
in you

the laughter of God
is surrounding your face
the laughter of God
in this time in this place
the laughter of God
drowns me in the embrace
in your laugh
in your laughter
in you

Charlie: journal

Arturo Ui

There, Charles. That wasn't so bad, was it? I think I can safely say I almost enjoyed that. Pulse still steady. Heart didn't flutter over-much. God, I'm sounding more like my Grandfather with every sentence. Every delaying sentence. And every successive delaying sentence. Right then (go away Grandfather—I will not have your ghost that you wouldn't have believed in, reading over my shoulder and commenting thus). Well, Joel. Ready for this one? Still delaying of course. But getting closer.

Wait for me. I'm serious. Please wait.

Charlie: filmscript 28

Uncomfortable

Charlie and Joel in the kitchen. It's 1971, just after Finals. They are discussing a play they've just seen; Brecht's Arturo Ui. *There is a copy of the programme lying on the kitchen table.*

Description of kitchen scene maybe?

CHARLIE
But the production is utterly, utterly wonderful.

209

JOEL

I'm not denying that. Of course. Yes. I'm just saying I'm left feeling un-comfortable.

CHARLIE

But that's the whole point. To feel uncomfortable. To be uncomfortable. Alienated. Clear thinking. Analytical.

JOEL

Yes, I know the theory, Charlie. I've written adulatory essays about the theory. And for some of his other plays I can applaud the practice.

CHARLIE

But?

JOEL

But with this one I'm not so sure. The material's too close to home.

CHARLIE

So you want to leave your brains with your hat and your coat in the cloakroom?

JOEL

Yes, I've used that quote too. I like it. I like the simplicity of it.

CHARLIE

So?

JOEL

It feels wrong not to feel the suffering. That's all I'm saying. For me. Right here. Right now. I feel—

CHARLIE

Don't say it—dear Joel—please don't say it.

JOEL

But I do—I feel guilty.

CHARLIE

But feelings are unreliable, Joel. You know that. That's what these plays are all about. What they demonstrate. A critique of mindless empathy. Not just in the theatre, for heaven's sake. In life.

JOEL

I suppose I believe there's a time and a place to keep your distance, a time and a place for analysis, and a time and a place for—

CHARLIE
For what?

JOEL
A time and a place to feel the pain.

CHARLIE
Why? What useful purpose does that serve?

JOEL
It serves no practical purpose—

CHARLIE
Exactly.

JOEL
But it means something. It means—

a pause

It means—

It means—

And there, dear friend, I take my leave. I cannot, for the life of me (and yes this is, this was my life), I cannot for the life of me remember what the hell it was you said after that. Send me a postcard, drop me a line, stating point of view. I'm hanging by a spider's thread here, dangling, like this conversation, between the present and the past, and with only a hazy glimmer of a future.

Wait for me. Dear friend. I will call. Please wait.

Rinchen, Joel

Rinpoche knows

—Hey Mr Joel.

—Hey hey *wunderkind.*

—Has Charlie called you yet?

—Not yet *kinderlach.*

—Do you think he will?

—I think he might.

—Would you like that?

—I would like it—yes I would—but that's not the point of it.

—What is the point of it?

—Can you work that out for yourself maybe?

—If you say so Mr Joel. Rinpoche says all the time it's good to work it out for yourself.

—Rinpoche knows.

—Yes. Rinpoche knows.

July 2004

Charlie, Hattie

Are you happy?

—Are you happy, Hattie?

—What an odd question, Charlie, why do you ask?

—I feel I can't feel your presence any more, you seem withdrawn.

—Well, I'm not unhappy. But it's a good question, and thank you for asking it.

—So give me a good answer, dear heart, I need some good answers at the moment.

—And specifically what sort of answer do you want?

—There is a gap between us; I would like that to heal. I want to reach out and take your hand. Metaphorically, that is. But I don't know where you are.

—Well, mostly I am thinking about my father. And, frankly, I could do with a hand. Literally as well as metaphorically. I am holding back from you because you have been so ill, but if you're ready to give me a hand I could really do with it.

—I think I'm ready, my love, I sort of hope and think I am ready.

—When I can see for myself that you truly are ready I will ask for your help. In the meantime, don't worry about it. I can manage on my own if I have to.

Hattie, Joel

I think it's time

—What do you think, Joel?

—I think it's time, Hattie.

—Time for what?

—Time for the truth, *liebchen*.

—Oh Joel, you haven't called me that since—

—Yes, I know.

—Yes, of course you do. Is he strong enough to take it?

—Yes. And it will help him be well quicker if you stop protecting him.

—I've been protecting myself too—it's not just kindness.

—Yes it is.

—What do you mean?

—You've been being kind to yourself. That's not a problem.

—Only for the Hattie Tattersall self-image. Pride, I suppose.

—Pride indeed *liebchen*. Nothing unusual in pride.

Hattie, Joel

Let me go

—Joel. Joel?

—I'm listening.

—I'm afraid.

—Afraid of what?

—Breakdown.

—Charlie's?

—No, Mine.

—And what would break?

—Me. All of me.

—Did you break last time?

—Yes. No. Maybe.

—And the time before that?

—Same. Same maybe.

—Exactly. Time to let me go now.

—You? Let you go?

—No. Let 'me' go.

—And then?

—And then, if there is still a then, there's that poem.

—Which poem?

—Ariel Andrews—remember—her reworking of Rumi.

—Really? No I don't remember.

—Look in the back of my copy of *Memories, Dreams, Reflections*—I wrote it down there for us.

—Did you? When?

—Ages ago.

Ariel Andrews: translation

From Rumi

> Out there, beyond
> the wrong and the right
> there is a meadow
> and there we will meet;
> when the soul lies down on that grass
> the world is too full for words:
> ideas, language, you, me
> are no more.
> Rumi

Rinchen, Hattie

Sing me that song

—Mum?

—Darling?

—Sing me that song again

—Which one this time?

—The Vaudeville Satori Blues please.

—OK. Why particularly right now?

—Because I like it and you need to hear it.

—Do I?

—Obviously.

Hattie: song

The vaudeville satori blues

It ain't been in vain—it ain't been in vain
no it ain't been in vain
for nothin'
this lovin'—it ain't been—it ain't been in vain
for nothin'
lovin' you—will see me through—my life

made you laugh babe, made you cry
made you think that we could fly
made you see we could defy—gravity
that gravity—the gravity—of life

in the sunshine, in the rain
through the heartache, through the pain
you and I we still defy—gravity
that gravity—the gravity—of life

it ain't been in vain—it ain't been in vain
no it ain't been in vain
for nothin'
this lovin'—it ain't been—it ain't been in vain
for nothin'
lovin' you—will see me through—my life

made me laugh babe, made me cry
made me stop and wonder why
made me see I could defy—gravity

that gravity—the gravity—of life
through the tumbles, through the falls
knowing we can walk up walls
you and I we still defy—gravity
that gravity—the gravity—of life

so it ain't been in vain—it ain't been in vain
no it ain't been in vain
for nothin'
this lovin'—it ain't been—it ain't been in vain
for nothin'
lovin' you—will see me through—my life

Rinchen, Hattie

Cosmo

—Did you write it for Charlie?

—Yes dear—and for a man called Cosmo—a man who walked up walls and danced like a mischievous angel and had a truly beautiful face.

—What sort of face?

—A sadfunny face. A face that defied gravity.

—And where did you meet him?

—I've never met him—he was a character in a movie called *Singin' in the Rain.*

—Oh him—I saw that at Annabel's house.

—Did you like it?

—I liked the funny bits—I loved the awesome bits. The bits that previous Charlie would do. I know what vaudeville means. What does satori mean?

—Better ask Joel, *liebchen.*

Rinchen, Joel

Googling satori

—Hey Mr Joel, where have you been?

—Nowhere very special *wunderkind*. Where have you been?

—Is Nowhereveryspecial a real place? I've been on the internet.

—It's as real as maybe. Did you enjoy the ride?

—Yes thank you. I was googling.

—What did you google?

—I googled satori.

—And did you find it?

—I found loads of satori Joel.

—That's my girl.

—I found a software company called it.

—And what do they specialise in precious?

—They specialise in standalone solutions.

—Ah. Sounds good to me.

—Do you have a standalone problem Joel?

—No. I can truthfully say I do not.

—Does Mum? I think perhaps she does.

—Why not ask her, *liebchen*.

—I think perhaps I will.

Rinchen, Hattie

Indra

—Mum?

—Yes, dear child of my heart.

—Do you have a standalone problem that needs a solution?

—How did you guess?

—Indra. I think Indra told me.

Rinchen, Joel

The laugh

—Joel?

—Back so soon?

—Yes, are you busy?

—Never too busy for you. You know that, don't you?

—Yes. Yes, I do; thank you.

—So what can I do for you?

—Satori.

—Yours for the asking.

—Thank you. What is it please? Really?

—That was it.

—What was?

—That laugh.

—Which laugh?

—The laugh you did just before the last 'thank you.'

—I didn't notice the laugh

—Exactly.

Rinchen, Hattie

Satori?

—Mum?

—Darling.

—Do you know what satori is?

—I do and I don't.

—Why is that?

—Because it is and it isn't.

—Isn't it?

Rinchen, Charlie

Right where you are

—Charlie?

—Hello, Rinchen.

—Do you know what satori is?

—I know how to describe it.

—Is that different?

—Yes. I think it is. I know enough about it to know that.

—Well please would you describe it to me please?

—Well, so far as I understand it, it's a sort of magical moment when time disappears, the world makes sense but not in words, and a feeling that's like joy, but is much bigger and better than joy fills you up completely. Only words like 'bigger' and 'better' no longer have much meaning. It's when what people call 'the mystery' is revealed and is not mysterious at all, but isn't anything else either. Your mind and body are all joined up so that you have no memory that you once thought they weren't and somehow you are everywhere in the universe at once and nowhere at all except right where you are.

—You mean like Cosmo—when he's leaping off the chair?

—You read my mind, Rinchen. You read my mind.

—Have you heard the song?

—Which song?

—Mum's vaudeville satori song

—Did she write one? She said she would once. No I haven't heard it.

—Ask her to sing it to you Charlie. It's very blues satori.

Rinchen, Hattie

It starts with a dream

—Mum?

—Hello, Rinchen.

—Have you had a satori experience?

—I have. Have you?

—Lots. Tell me one of yours.

—Let me read it to you. This is one I wrote in my diary about nine years ago. It starts with a dream.

I'm walking in the forest again. It's so familiar now. It's springtime and the birds are singing. I am alone.

I come to a clearing, and sweet sunlight is breaking through. Three big plane trees mark out a circular stage. I go and stand in their grand enclosure and breathe freely. Up till this point I must have been holding my breath—but I didn't realise it till I felt the exquisite freedom of this new deep breath. The air is surprisingly mild and comfortable. I think it might be that little clearing in Fontaine de Vaucluse—behind the Petrarch museum. There is a little sparkling river somewhere to the side of me. I can hear its bubbling melody and harmonic overtones play like fireflies in flight—intense coloured lights that flash even brighter than the sunlight. I begin to dance. At first quite slowly and then with intensity. A new dance.

A rabbit comes out from the trees—a rabbit with big brown eyes and a look in his eyes as old as time. I pause in my dance, in a pose like Shiva, and meet his gaze. We hold each other in astonishment and love. Amazed perfection. Perfect amazement. Perfect. A moment or an aeon passes. And suddenly—oh, the word makes no sense in this timeless place. Let's say a fresh moment arises and there is a sudden realisation that there is absolutely no distinction between the rabbit and me. There is just this blissful and blessed moment of everything and nothing. It is the springtime of the world again.

Next day, Rinpoche calls and tells me he has a job for me.

What is it? I ask. He laughs and says he will come and see me.

—That was me wasn't it? Rinpoche meant me.

—Yes. The most precious job I could ever want.

—Have you shown that diary to Charlie?

—No. Not yet. Do you think I should?

—Obviously.

Hattie, Charlie

The missing years

—How are you today Charlie?

—Fit as a fiddle dearest. Legs getting stronger by the minute. Mind and heart in sync. Sync as in Fred and Ginger. Not as in kitchen.

—Fit enough to read this?

—Undoubtedly. What is it?

—Some stuff I'd like you to know now.

—Hattie Tattersall the missing years?

—Exactly.

—Are you sure? Are you certain you want me to see this?

—Do you mind?

—Will it help?

—I think so.

—Then I'm at your service. Leave it with me. I'll read it straight away.

—I'm sorry, Charlie.

—Whatever for?

—For not speaking sooner. For not staying close. For not trusting our love and friendship. For being too proud.

Rinchen, Charlie

Sitting with

—Hello, Charlie

—Hello, Rinchen

—We've come to sit with you.

—We?

—Me and the Following Cat.

—Where is he?

—He's following.

—So he is. How kind.

—Is that your rogue and peasant slave speaking?

—It's my Sir John impersonation—you remember.

—Why are you doing an actor voice, Charlie?

—Because I'm afraid my heart might break, Rinchen.

—Heartbreak is all right Charlie. Sometimes it's better than all right.

—Is it?

—Yes. But the breaking has to be from love. Not from fear.

—Did Rinpoche tell you that?

—No. Joel did.

—Is that why you've come to sit with me? You and the Following Cat?

—Yes Charlie. Read now.

Hattie: letter

I didn't want anyone to know

July 2004

Dearest Charlie—my longtime closest friend, this is a very difficult letter for me to write—but I know it's the right thing to do, and actually, it's a great relief. I should have told you the truth ages ago. Well, at the time really—we'd always been so honest with one another. But for some reason I just couldn't bring myself to do it. I started letters—but then you'd call to see how I was doing, and I would hear myself putting on the bright, Mancunian Hattie Tattersall 'I can do anything I choose' voice, and would hear us, with consummate ease, fall into our familiar roles. And, actually, for a few glorious minutes, I would really believe that all was well, and that nothing had disrupted our joyful lives. Crazy—but then, I was. So here my love—several years too late—is the truth of what was happening for me when you were in America.

I'd like to think I was keeping this from you because I truly just wanted you to be free and happy and fully engaged in the excitement of the work you were doing in New York and Boston—and maybe, just maybe, some of that was there. But mostly I didn't want anyone to know how bad I was feeling. It was difficult enough having been so ill and exhausted that the band had to fold. And, if I'm being ruthlessly honest, I didn't know how to say I needed help. So, my dear, my closest friend, here—with more love than you can imagine—here is a letter I wrote to you at the time, and some diary entries that I wrote with you in mind—you and Joel—always always you and Joel—and didn't send. It did help me to write them.

Hattie: letter

My dear true friend

6 June 1988

Dear Charlie, my dear true friend. This is a letter you'll never receive because the only way I can write it is to know that I'll never send it. It was so sweet of you to call, and so difficult talking to you on the phone yesterday. New York seems a long way away, and your life there so full and so unreachable.

How I wish you were here so I could just hold you, and be held by you, and you would somehow see me through this.

There's no easy way to say this and no place to start—so I'll start with the hardest thing. Two days ago I had a miscarriage. No-one but Mark knew I was pregnant. And no-one else knows that the baby died. He's been kind of course, but he doesn't really understand. He's not Joel. He's not you.

Probably it was foolish to even think of having a child. The fatigue is no better. The pains still ongoing, but life with Mark has been a sweet oasis and—well—why am I even bothering to try and explain it—we simply thought a baby would be a good idea. I'm too tired to write any more to-night. I'm so glad I started though. Thank you as always my closer than life friend.

Rinchen, Charlie

All right now

—Charlie?

—Sweetheart.

—It's all right you know.

—Is it? Is it, precious?

—It's all right now.

—Right now, right here with you and the Following Cat—what could be more perfect?

—Yes Charlie. Read more now.

Hattie: journal

I knew she had died

I knew she had died. I woke in the night and knew I was alone in my body again. At first I hoped I was dreaming—that I would swim to the surface of this moonlit water and find myself in another place, another time, with my baby safe within me still. But as I waited and listened to the familiar sounds of the room and the house, seeing the sky begin to breathe its way towards dawn, I knew I was me awake and alone. She had slipped away whilst I was sleeping. I felt that if only I'd stayed awake I could have caught the moment—maybe I could have held her for a few moments longer—maybe not. But at least I could have said goodbye. It was too late. There was nothing left. No-one left.

Later, much later, when the blood came, it was a relief at first. I thought that I would feel freer somehow. But there was so much blood. And I hadn't expected that. And because I knew by then that she had gone—gone far away—I wasn't expecting to see her body. Foolish, I know—but I wasn't expecting it. She was so tiny. So precious. So dead. It was her hands that touched me the most. Such amazing hands. I'll never forget the love I felt for those hands. The love I feel now. For a moment—a long moment—she was as alive for me as she had ever been, because I knew what those hands were capable of—music—healing—loving. Such generous hands. Lifeless and cold in mine.

Oh Charlie—I wish you were here. I wish Joel were here.

Rinchen, Charlie

Shall we call Joel?

—Charlie. Charlie?

—Mmn.

—Shall we call Joel?

—Not yet precious. I'm not ready yet.

—OK Charlie.

Hattie: journal

It hurts to write now

3 July 1988

It hurts to write now. My hands hurt. My head hurts. Everything hurts. This vast yawning emptiness. This hollow shell. No more songs. No more music. Even the rhythms have disappeared. I no longer expect melodies, but I can't hear any rhythms any more. Just this screaming silence. I can't bear it.

Hattie: journal

The house is quiet

9 July 1988

Strange to be home all this time. Strange not to be on tour. Strange to be here with just Mark. He is kindness itself. I wish I had more to give. The house is quiet. The fatigue is slightly less today. I have read a little. My head hurts too much to read more. Joel's voice is near though. I can almost hear him. Maybe I'm getting better now.

Hattie: journal

Where have the dreams gone?

4 September 1988

Mark left. I understand why. In a way I'd left him. In a way I'd never been fully present for him. It doesn't feel any different without him. Should it? The phone's been ringing. Maybe it's Charlie. I can't do the cheerful voice today. Maybe it's Mum or Dad. I can't do the 'please don't worry about me' script either. Can't do anything. Must sleep. Must sleep now. Where have the dreams gone? I think I might feel better if there were dreams.

Hattie: letter

I knew

12 February 1989

Dear Charlie, dear Joel

You need to know this. Mum died last night.

I knew she had died. I woke in the early morning. Too hot. Too cold. And got out of bed. Restless. Anxious. Not like myself. More like her. Her as she has become since she's been unwell. Since the illness has been speaking through her. She wanted me to hear something. I sat quietly in the window seat, and tried to listen. Couldn't get it. Just this restlessness, this pulsing worry, this ghastly silent void.

The phone rang. It was still early. Too early for anything other than bad news. It was Dad—but not his usual voice. Far away and bewildered. So then I really knew. But what was she trying to say? Why can't I hear? What's wrong with me?

Oh, my dear loves. Where are you? I can't send this. I don't know what to do. I don't know who I am any more. Someone please help me.

How will I manage? How will I get to Manchester? Dad needs me. I have to manage something somehow. Someone please help me

Hattie: journal

All of me gone

3 March 1989

I have no clear recollection of the funeral. I know I've been in Manchester. Mark drove me there. Stayed. Helped. Dad isn't Dad. I'm not Hattie. It's raining. It's cold. This huge house rattles its windows at me. Someone is in the kitchen. There is food by my bedside. I can't eat it. Too tired. Too tired. Nothing left. Nobody at home. Hattie Tattersall has left the building. All of me gone. Gone. Gone.

Rinchen, Charlie

Not

—Charlie, me and the cat, shall we come closer?

—That would be—that would be—

—Well, we think we will.

—I like it that you hum and he purrs, precious.

—Yes. We're a band.

—Really? What are you called?

—Not.

—Not?

—We're not called.

—What do you mean?

—They don't call us.

—Ah! You mean you call them?

—Exactly.

—Oh precious. You are sunshine itself.

—Read now Charlie. Read. Finish the story.

Hattie: journal

Liberation of the dancers

April 18 1989

Last night I dreamed. I am awake now and maybe still dreaming. Like Pericles. Like Charlie's Pericles. If this is madness, I prefer it to so called sanity. Charlie, Joel, please hear my dream.

Who am I? I am the ocean. Waves come and waves go. Waves come and waves go. They curl, they intersect, they crash in opposing forces. I give them attention when they call. I play in the surf. I examine minutely the flotsam and jetsam. I swim by the vastness of the singing whales and play catch me if you can with the benevolently smiling snub-nosed dolphins. I am tickled by the quick, blinking movements of glittering fish. I accept the harsh interplay of shark and prey. And pray. For them. For us. For the enduring dance of birth and rebirth. For the liberation of the dancers.

But I am always conscious that I am ocean. The mind flows in its waves. Life presents the apparency of things that come and go. In life I play with it all. But I am ocean. Ocean always. Simultaneous and infinite.

Hattie: journal

Lifeline

19 April 1989

This morning I called Joel. This time I got through. Straight away.

—Hattie—*liebchen.*

—Joel?

—Toujours.

—Where are you? Are you busy?

—Nowhere special. Never too busy for you *liebchen*. Here for you. Always here for you.

Then the line went dead. But it was enough. It was heaven. It was a lifeline. And later I wrote a song. Or maybe he wrote it? I'm not sure. It doesn't matter. Nothing, nothing matters. Nothing matters more than this—this thin, pale hint of something like life, something like meaning, something like hope. Maybe it's the springtime of the world? Maybe Charlie will come with us? Please Charlie—somehow? It has to be the three of us. That's how it's always been. Always.

Hattie: song

The song: the laurel shall grow green

there will come a measured time
there will be a treasured place
there will be a moment when
the skylark will appear

there will come a measured time
there will be a treasured place
there will be a moment when

the skylark's song is clear

and I know that we'll remember
all the promises we made
for the seasons keep on turning
till it's time to meet again

and the truth shall then be spoken
in the springtime of the world
and the laurel shall grow green again
the laurel shall grow green

Hattie, Joel

Our song

22 April 1989

—Joel?

—Here we are, Hattie.

—Do you like the song?

—I do.

—It's our song, isn't it? You, me, Charlie.

—It is, *liebchen,* it is.

Hattie: journal

Fearless simplicity

24 April 1989

Dear Charlie, dear Joel—the dreams are happening. The songs too. It won't be long before we meet again, will it? I dreamed last night of Ely Cathedral. Why Ely? Ariel Andrews—goodness, I haven't thought of her in a long while—Ariel would point out the similarity between Ely and Eli—one of the names of God. I seem to be getting a brain back. Thank goodness. Ely was a sweet place to be—in the early days of Crazy Wisdom Lady—remember that gig in Cambridge?—some festival or other. We were thrilled to have the work—they loved us. East Anglia seemed vast and flat and somehow very foreign. We took a little holiday—Ely—

Norwich—Cromer. Ate fish on the beach cooked on that little camping stove—the smallest stove in the known universe. And sky—so much sky over that strange flat landscape. We were in love with it all. Here's my dream. Enjoy. *L'chaim* Joel. *L'chaim* Charlie.

We are in Ely Cathedral—me, Charlie, a little fragile girl and someone behind me that I can't quite see. It is early morning and wintertime. The light is soft and pale through the clear glass. We turn towards the Lady Chapel and that amazing statue—so big and bold and strong.

Prayers are happening somewhere and I notice a humming sound that fills the air with fearless simplicity.

I turn to look at the child—but she has vanished. I turn back to Charlie—but he has vanished too.

The sound remains. I am washed in sound and the dazzling complexity of colour as the morning sunlight hits the azure and golden allure of the coloured glass above the east wall.

There is still someone behind me that I can't quite see. I know I am not alone.

Hattie: journal

Walking in the forest again

1 August 1995

Was this a dream? Is it a memory? I can't tell. No matter. It's as real and as numinous as maybe. More real than real. Can I capture it on paper? Just.

I'm walking in the forest again. It's so familiar now. It's springtime and the birds are singing. I am alone. Not sad. Not happy.

I come to a clearing, and sweet sunlight is breaking through. Three big plane trees mark out a circular stage. I go and stand in their grand enclosure and breathe freely. Up till this point I must have been holding my breath—but I didn't realise it till I felt the exquisite freedom of this new deep breath. The air is surprisingly mild and comfortable. I think it might be that little clearing in Fontaine de Vaucluse—behind the Petrarch museum. There is a little sparkling river somewhere to the side of me. I can hear its bubbling melody and harmonic overtones play like fireflies in flight—intense coloured lights that flash even brighter than the sunlight. I begin to dance. At first quite slowly and then with intensity. A new graceful dance.

A rabbit comes out from the trees—a rabbit with big brown eyes and a look in his eyes as old as time. I pause in my dance, in a pose like Shiva, and meet his gaze. We hold each other in astonishment and love. Amazed perfection. Perfect amazement. Perfect. A moment or an aeon passes. And suddenly—oh, the word makes no sense in this timeless place. Let's say a fresh moment arises and there is a sudden realisation that there is absolutely no distinction between the rabbit and me. There is just this blissful and blessed moment of everything and nothing. It is the springtime of the world again.

This morning, Rinpoche called and told me he has a job for me. 'What is it?' I ask. He laughs and says he will come and see me.

Rinchen, Charlie

The me story

—That's the me story isn't it Charlie?

—Yes, precious. Yes it is.

—Mum told it me yesterday. Do you like it?

—I love it. I really love it.

—We're going now. Me and the Following Cat. Did your heart break enough?

—I think it did. What do you think?

—I think you need to be on your own to do crying now.

—Yes. Thank you Rinchen.

—I love you, Charlie.

—I love you too.

Rinchen, Charlie

Green tear white tear

—Charlie—are you busy?

—Never too busy for my precious girl. Back so soon? Why so serious?

—Rinpoche said I had to tell you a story. He said it was important. Important—serious and right away.

—Well, here we are—I'm listening.

—Are you listening serious? Serious all the way through?

—Never more so.

—OK. Well the story goes like this. You know that picture that Mum has by the long window in her room?

—That beautiful man with four hands?

—Yes—that one. Rinpoche says he's called Chenrezig. He's a Buddha of Compassion. He's very important. And—

—*Om mani peme hung?*

—Yes! How did you know that, Charlie?

—I've known your Mum a long time, you know.

—OK. OK. Do you know the green tear white tear story?

—No, dear. Tell me.

—Well, Chenrezig saw suffering—suffering everywhere—whole worlds full of suffering. Too much. Too much.

—Yes, love, too much.

—And he made this big promise that he would get it all sorted. No more suffering. And he tried and he tried—three big times—but he couldn't. Not even though he was amazing and magic and strong and fearless. Can't be done, he said, can't be done. So you know what?

—No—what, precious?

—So he sat down and cried. Two huge beautiful tears—one green tear and one white. And they turned into two woman Buddhas—called Green Tara and White Tara. And if you need help with the suffering, they come with the speed of wind to anyone who calls on them for help. Straight away. No problem. That's their job.

It's good to cry Charlie. Cry the green tears white tears. They will come. It's their job.

August 2004

Joel, Hattie

Face the fear

—What are you waiting for, Hattie?

—I'm not sure, Joel. For the right moment perhaps? For some sort of sign that I have permission to do this.

—Whose permission do you need?

—My Father's. It's his secret. Perhaps I should just let it go? Bury the box somewhere special to him? Burn it maybe?

—What are you frightened of?

—How do you know it's fear?

—Because you're shaking.

—Oh—yes—so I am. Help me. Tell me what to do?

—Face the fear. Dive straight into it and see it for what it is.

Hattie, Joel

Go straight forward

—I am faced by a terrible, aching void. I am cold and alone on a hill top somewhere. It is dark. So dark I can't even see myself.

—Go forwards, Hattie. Go straight forward.

—It's colder and somehow darker still. I am being pulled towards the huge empty corridor of no light.

—What do you hear?

—I hear the humming of my own blood pulsing against my ears. I feel sick with dread.

—Keep going. You're doing fine.

—It's like walking through dense clammy fog. Hard to breathe. Hard to move, even—the altitude is unfamiliar. My head is throbbing. I think the words 'I can't do this', but I know I can. I just don't want to. Or rather some part of me doesn't want to.

—Good. You're getting there.

—OK yes—it's getting lighter and easier to breathe. The corridor sensation is lessening—there's more space somehow. Still quite dark though.

—What do you hear?

—I hear singing. Oh Joel, I hear the song. I hear it!

—The song?

—Yes—our Provençal song. Oh Joel, I don't think I can bear it.

Hattie, Joel

Open it

—OK, Joel. Today's the day. This moment is the moment. Whatever it is I can bear it. I know what I know. I know my father was the best possible father and the best possible human being. If there is some dark secret that needs to be revealed, then that changes nothing.

—Exactly.

—I wonder why he didn't speak before, though. What can it be that had to be kept secret till now?

—Open it, Hattie darling. Just open it.

—OK I'll do the recent envelope first, shall I?

—That makes sense. Yes. The new envelope.

Jack: letter

Looking back

9 April 2004

Dearest Hattie, I found these papers when I was setting my affairs in order so that you won't have any mess to clear up after I am dead, my dear. I never sent them to you, and I asked Joel not to tell you about the conversation we had, over that cup of tea, thirty years ago, in the café at New Street Station.

Cowardice? Perhaps. You will judge, my love, because now is the time to tell you: the time also for me to confront what happened in Spain, as I sit here now, with my whisky and my pills and my cancer; and such strength of mind as I have.

Jack: letter

Jack and Joel

6 April 1972

I am writing this, my dearest daughter, on the evening after my foolish expedition to Birmingham. I am profoundly ashamed of some things I said about your friends, and in particular, as you will see, I deeply and bitterly regret what I said about your friend Joel. Charlie is a nice young man, with beautiful manners, highly intelligent, funny, and kind. I have no doubts about him, in spite of his wealth and his appalling accent. He is a good man. Joel too; but more. As the evening went on—and I really enjoyed myself, love, it was grand—there was something about Joel; something deep, something that disturbed me, shook my foundations. That quiet that he has, that delicate quick certainty, that sense of goodness—it was familiar to me, somehow: it reminded me. Of what?

I found out next morning, when he took me to the station. Driving into town in that ridiculous hippie van, he said, suddenly:

—You were in the Spanish Civil War, I believe.

Well, you know how I am about that. Quite fiercely, in fact (I have to say it) very rudely, I said

—I don't talk about it.

—Yes, he said. I understand. I only mention it because I think you may have known my uncle.

—Your uncle? I said, still bristling, like a ridiculous hedgehog.

—Emmanuel Cohen; Manny—Manny Cohen.

I truly cannot describe the effect that had on me. When you have read this message through, you will understand why. I was speechless. Eventually, spluttering, foolish, I said:

—You are Manny Cohen's nephew?

—Yes, he said, simply. We still talk about him, in the family. I grew up hearing about him. You could say, I think, that from him, from those stories, I learned how to live.

Well, Hattie, my love, you won't believe this. I cried. I put my face in my hands and I absolutely sobbed, as you have never seen me, my whole body shaking, convulsed. Joel stopped the car, and just sat there, quietly, until I got control of myself again. When things had calmed down, he said, smiling slightly:

—I take it that you knew my uncle, then?

—Oh yes, I said, laughing, crying, Oh yes, I think you could say that.

And he laughed too, and we went and had a cup of tea.

Jack: letter

Jack's story: how to tell it?

6 April 1972

It is now time to tell you my story. I have always presumed to be your teacher, dear Hattie; though your talent and your beautiful mind have taken you beyond my teaching, and in directions that I could not have imagined. You are your own woman, and I am proud of you. But here, with humility, with respect, is one particular lesson.

Why have I not told you this story before? It is the story of Spain, my dear, as I saw it. I have never spoken of it for a simple reason. Violence is wrong. Killing is wrong. War is an obscenity. But I cannot speak about Spain without speaking of those comrades who died, and my admiration for their selfless courage. I think of them as heroes and martyrs. Even now, I cannot bear it, that I have lived on, and left so many fine comrades behind. But to glorify them, as they deserve, is to glorify war. I will not glorify war.

I don't tell war stories. I don't tell anti-war stories either, they're one and the same. If you want a war story, read Hemingway. Or, preferably, don't.

However, I do have a story. I want you to know about it. But, how to tell it?

History. We used to talk a lot about history, in those days. History will absolve us, we thought. Like a priest, you know? Well, I was part of a historic event, I fought in the British Battalion in the Spanish civil war at the battle of the Jarama River, and, dear Hattie, I know, like anyone knows who has taken part in any event like that, that history is chaos. There is no such thing as history; there are only historians, telling their stories, contradicting each other, selecting their facts from the bewildering ebb and flow of circumstance.

I will tell you. Here is my history. All those years ago. Here is my fiction, Hattie; here is my dream.

Jack: letter

Jack's story: the rifle

You must understand how *young* I was. I was ignorant, I had never been out of England. I knew nothing whatsoever about how to fight, how to fire a gun, how to stop myself being killed; how to kill.

I remember my rifle. They gave them to us at the last moment, this was before the Russian weapons came through, and what they gave us was terrible: old, battered, broken. Dirty. I was proud to have that excuse for a weapon. I was proud of its battle-scarred appearance, ignorant fool that I was: I thought it was *supposed* to be dirty. I carried the gun through the streets of Figueras—God, it was heavy: they don't tell you about that in the books—with a little group of friends, all working class lads from Manchester, holding these heavy menacing objects, these tatty guarantors of manhood, feeling brave and righteous, and wondering what on earth to do with ourselves.

Eventually we decided the occasion merited a drink. So we went into a café, not knowing what the hell to do when we got there, and, you know, it didn't matter: as soon as we set foot in the place we were amongst friends. Amongst comrades. Such joy, that was.

I had never tasted wine before. Still less had I poured it into my mouth from a miniature watering can held a foot away from my face. The laughter was considerable. The songs began, back-slapping, clenched fists raised, the war was as good as won and all the fascists had run away; they would see us and hear our songs and recognise our obvious rectitude, and they would turn and run. It was wonderful. We really believed that, you know.

There was a man sitting in the corner, a little quiet man, observant, unobtrusive, with a stillness about him; a tough stillness. After a while, he came over to me, introduced himself, amid the noise and wine and laughter; he spoke quietly, but you could hear every word he said. After a minute of chat, where are you from, how did you get here, he said this:

—We go to the line in two days time.

—The line?

—The front. Where the fighting is.

It was something about the way he said it. He knew what he was talking about. I was sober, instantly.

That was Manny Cohen.

—Your weapon needs cleaning, Comrade. If you fire it like that, the bullet could explode in the breech, and kill you.

I looked at him, with horror, with shame. He met my gaze calmly, without recrimination. His gaze was utterly—*selfless*. He had nothing to prove. He held out his hand for the gun, and I gave it to him—by this time I was in a state of shock.

His hands *flowed* over the grimy weapon, that's the only way I can describe it, and it came apart. He looked down the barrel, winced, and showed it to me: partly blocked with dirt. Lethal. Lethal to me, that is.

—How did you learn how to do that? I said. He smiled.

—I learned it at school, he said. I couldn't believe it.

—At school? At my school you were lucky if you learned how to read.

—Yes, Comrade, he said: they don't teach the workers how to use weapons, for some reason; only the sons of the rich. Meet me tomorrow, you and your friends, and I will teach you as much as I know.

And he did; he saved my life. Oh, and it turned out he was the company commander. That was the kind of army it was.

Jack: letter

Jack's story: the hill

We marched to a farmhouse, at the foot of a hill. Spent the night there, not sleeping much, wondering. We had no idea; we had no idea.

Next morning, we walked up the hill. The fascists wanted Madrid; we were in the way. We, the British Battalion, just happened to be at the weakest point of the line, the place where they decided to attack.

They attacked the hill, and we had to hold it. Now, these were seasoned soldiers, coming at us; not volunteers, not conscripts: professionals. Seasoned, vicious, highly efficient, killers. They knew what they were doing. Maybe, even, they liked it. We were a ridiculous collection of complete amateurs: coalminers and poets. We didn't know what we were doing. We held the hill.

What is combat like? You can't imagine. Being subjected to devastating firepower: artillery, machine guns, aimed rifle fire, aeroplanes. All of that they threw at us.

Combat is *wrong*. Terrible things, *wrong* things, happen. It is wrong that people should die, should scream, should kill, should lose limbs, should be blown open. The *smells* are wrong: shit, corruption, blood, fear. It is a catastrophic wrongness.

Try to imagine a train crash. Suddenly, from nowhere, enormous violence, noise, chaos, the devastating effects of machinery on human bodies, blood, screaming, destruction. Cacophony. Well, combat is like that. Except it doesn't stop. Or, it stops only to start again. And: in the middle of it you have to keep an absolutely clear head, act resolutely and rationally, and fight back. And not run away.

That went on for three days. That was our introduction to war. Some historians say that battle was the worst of the whole Spanish war. It was certainly truly terrible.

What kept us on that hill? Why did we not run back to the farmhouse, away from the train crash? Comradeship. Love. I will say no more about that, I will not dishonour that love with the inadequacy of words. I will just say this, that all the rest of my life I have tried to live by that love.

Manny Cohen epitomised it. During the night—can you imagine, what the night was like, knowing now what the morning would bring?—he was there, quiet, calm, understated, humorous. Sharing, supporting. Showing us what socialism was like. He was an unbelievably good man.

On the third day it got worse. The Russians on our left fell back, and we were in a cross fire. There was nowhere to hide. Many died. Of the 600 men who walked up that hill, wondering what would happen, smelling the thyme in that sunscorched landscape, brave, determined, greatly afraid, two out of every three were killed.

The order came to retreat. We carried the wounded, as well as we could, and fell back to the farmhouse; the fascists took the hill.

Exhausted, utterly drained, terribly shocked, we fell back. Collapsing on our feet, carrying our shattered comrades. Amazed to be alive.

Then the word came round—imagine, dearest, the exhausted shell-shocked men—the order came: attack. Unbelievable. Impossible. We were a defeated remnant, we were ruined.

You read of officers making inspiring speeches. We didn't have that kind of officer. We had Manny Cohen. He looked at us, and smiled.

—Come on, Comrades, he said; we must do this.

He picked up his gun and started to walk up the hill. What did we do? Of course, we followed him. Staggering with exhaustion, each man with the immediate personal knowledge of imminent certain death, we began to walk back up the hill. And: this. Just this. He started to sing. *The Internationale.* A lonely wavering voice. On my right the miners joined in, stronger, stronger, out of dry mouths and impossible tiredness somehow the words came. We sang, and walked up the hill towards the certainty of death.

And, Hattie, Hattie, that was what turned it. They thought we were fresh troops, you see, because of the singing, so they fell back. We held the hill, and kept Franco out of Madrid. For a while.

Of course, as they retreated they fought. They were professionals, and laid down covering fire to protect an orderly retreat. I caught the bullet that cost me my leg, and Manny Cohen was machine-gunned, and died instantly.

I do not think any more of the waste of that early death. I think only this: that every moment of my life must be lived in the selflessness that he taught me. Only then does anything make sense.

Jack: letter

More

9 April 2004

And that, my love, is the story I told Joel over the cup of tea. However, there is more than that, and the more than that is what caused me to ask for his silence, and what kept me from telling it to you for the whole of my long life.

I am happy and content, my dearest daughter. It is time for you to know everything. Read the next and final section of this letter, and then read the document in the box I gave to Owen for safe keeping. Then, I hope, you'll understand everything. Enough time has been measured now. Goodbye, goodnight.

Jack: letter

Cigarettes

As you know, I have devoted my life to socialism; and, as we both know, that dream is over. The world, quite casually, shrugged in its sleep, and away went Lenin and Soviet Russia and all those terrible fought-for certainties. Fought for, paid for; so much suffering. Gone, all gone. What is left? This is the story of what is left: of what was not destroyed by the terrible betrayals, the dreadful bloodstained history of a beautiful idea. This is why I stayed in the Party, in spite of all that happened.

Where to begin?

In those days, my dear, we used to smoke a lot. The working class had few pleasures, in the thirties, and one of them was smoking. Woodbines. Woodbines and strong raw red-brown tea, gallons of it; appetite killers, you see. I gave up the cigarettes years ago, as you know, when the truth started to come out; but all those Woodbines did their work, and now, at last, they are killing me. Well, you have to die of something, and I feel a certain solidarity with all those other workers killed by the profit motive—think of it, Hattie, just think of it: millions of them, killed by smog and black lung and asbestos and lead poisoning and on and on.

After I took the wound in my leg I was out of the war for good. And nearly died: field hospital conditions were pretty rough and ready. All right, I will tell the truth, they were dreadful. Pain, delirium, nightmare. Eventually I found myself in a hospital, in France—somehow they had got me out of Spain, I am still not clear how. And in that hospital there were no cigarettes and no tea. Sounds trivial, doesn't it, but that deprivation, of those crude necessities, nearly drove me over the edge.

In fact, I went mad, for a while, I think, in that hospital in the French Pyrenees. On a lonely hillside, forests, mists, sunlight, woodsmoke, the chill and clarity in the air, and a pervading sense of strangeness, as if the landscape was full of old secrets. While all around Europe was turning into a nightmare.

The news from Spain was bad, always bad; and then it got worse. Treachery, atrocity, on both sides. Destruction of the innocent. Then there was the memory of combat, in and out of my head. And then there was the pain. Yes, indeed, the pain. And, above all, there was remembering those friends and comrades who died on the hill, some of them I'd known since childhood, dying in a good cause that was now turning bad, but they were just as dead, just as lost, good cause or bad cause. Dead, all dead.

Oh, and the fear. We all had that. When would the bombers fly, all over Europe, dropping fire and poison gas and anthrax, destroying everything? What hope was there, what possibility? And the pain.

They drugged me, of course. It lessened the pain, from time to time, and accentuated the nightmare, the madness.

So: all of that was swirling round in my head, bewildering me, wearing me down, abrading my courage and my sense of logic and justice and of truth itself. It was dreadful. I sat in the hospital garden, and experienced complete despair.

Then something happened.

That something was, in fact, insanity, I now think. When I wrote it up, shortly afterwards, I thought otherwise. When I got back home, and gradually healed, and put my life into the struggle against fascism, regained my moral and intellectual equilibrium, I could see it for what it was: an outbreak of unreason. Since then I have always, as a secret fear, dreaded the return of this unreason; and, a deeper, even more secret fear, dreaded to see it surface in you, some corruption in the blood, in the mind, that I had passed on to you. So when you started talking about dreams, and the

Pyrenees, and the twelfth century, and mentioning casually, in a sideline, that you had taken drugs, you can imagine my horror and distress. That is what drove me to Birmingham, on that long ago visit, when I made a fool of myself in front of those good young men. Read the document I gave to Owen all those years ago, and you will see why.

Joel, Hattie

Never closer

—I think it would be good to read it now, *liebchen*.

—Yes. I know. Stay close, Joel. Very close.

—Never closer, Hattie. Open Jack's box.

Hattie

Are you listening?

—Oh Joel, I don't think I can go on. I thought I knew everything about my Dad. We were so close. He taught me everything. Told me everything. What is this secret he wants me to know? He wasn't a man who kept secrets. He told the truth. Always.

—Joel, Joel, Are you listening?

—Joel, where are you?

—Joel?

Jack: the letter in the box

Skylark

April 1937

I am sitting in a garden in France, my dear, writing to a daughter I have not yet met, or imagined, or conceived. Strange behaviour, you might say, for a materialist. You are right. However, I must write this, because I was told to do so, and you will read it, but only after I am dead. Because that is when you will need it, or so I have been told. Why am I doing this? To pay a debt. I always pay my debts.

I am in France because I was in a war. A battle: Jarama, it was called. I wonder if you have heard of it. I cannot tell you about it. See if you can find it in the history books. For me it is too raw, too dreadful; it is what happened a few weeks ago. I cannot bear to think of it. We won the battle, by the way. Many good friends and comrades died, some of them dreadfully. My company commander, Manny Cohen, a hero and a true socialist, the best man I have ever met, lost his life. This too I cannot bear to think of much. Oh, and I lost a leg.

That is why I am here, in France, in a pleasant garden. It is early evening, the light, fading, is magical, a little hallucinatory; but that could be the drugs, or the pain, or both. I am full of grief, and pain (sorry to keep mentioning this), and have never lived more intensely, nor ever will again; I am very happy. I may, of course, be mad; you must judge.

It happened exactly 24 hours ago, and I was sitting here, in this exact spot, working on the pain, my constant comrade. I have found that it is possible to withdraw the mind, so that the pain lessens. It needs very intense concentration, but it is possible. That is what I was doing, and with another part of my mind I was watching a bird, spiralling, up and up, into the un-English sky, the lurid blue, the neurotic Van Gogh blue. A skylark, surely: so that's what a skylark is like, I thought, as its song spun out from the spirals, scattering thin slivers and flakes of sound. I thought of that fool Shelley, and of Vaughan Williams of course, my mind spiralling and casting flakes of thought, around the hard unremitting struggle with the pain, and—

What? What the hell is *that*? The bird has stopped rising, and is starting to descend, but clumsily, as if it has forgotten how to fly. Has some bastard shot it? The French will eat anything, I know that. Down, look, down it comes, and it is—not a bird. Not a bird at all. It's a doll, a mannequin, a winged monkey. It's a man. It's a man with wings, dear God Jack Tattersall the opiates have rotted your brain, a man with wings, oh my God, it's—an angel.

I closed my eyes. Tight. I palmed them. Took deep breaths; called myself back from whatever lunacy I had fallen into, composed myself, got a grip, and, gradually, opened my eyes.

The angel had landed. It was standing in front of me. It was smiling, wryly, a familiar smile. It was Manny Cohen. Manny Cohen is dead. Manny

Cohen is stitched across with machine gun bullets and lying in a hasty grave at the foot of a hill in Spain.

—I don't believe this, I said. Or croaked.

—No. he said, I don't believe it, either, but I thought it would get your attention. And he shrugged his shoulders, and the wings fell away, and vanished.

—Have a Woodbine, he said, pulling out a battered packet.

—Manny, you're an illusion. You're dead. You died in Spain. I saw it.

—Yes, he said, yes to all of that. Have an illusory Woodbine.

He reached across, holding the packet, open. I could see the fine black hairs on the back of his hand. I looked up at him, at his wise witty utterly familiar face, and froze: I just didn't know what the hell to do.

—Go on, Jack, it's rude to refuse a friend: take a cigarette.

Mechanically, I lifted my hand, took the cool firm paper cylinder, pulled it out and put it in my mouth. He struck a match, and held it for me. I felt the heat, and the familiar catch in my throat as the acrid smoke went into my lungs. Nothing is more real than a cheap cigarette.

There were no wounds in his chest where the bullets had hit. I took his hand in mine, felt the warmth and firmness of his grip. It was real.

—Manny, I said, gripping his hand tightly, Manny, did you die?

—Yes, Jack, I did. That smile, patient, astute.

—Then what the hell are you doing in France?

—You need to talk to someone. I've come to fetch you. Will you come with me?

—This is not happening, I said. This is the morphine, and the shock. Or perhaps I am going mad.

—All of that is possible. Believe me, it's of no importance at all. Jack, come with me. Please?

Helplessly, I nodded. I owe that man my life, several times over. It was impossible to refuse. In some strange act of abandonment, I accepted the delusion, and let go of the material, sensible, believable world. I grasped his extremely real-seeming hand, tightly, like a lifeline.

—Yes, Manny, I said; if you say so, then yes.

And then we were somewhere else. A soft transition, as at the cinema, no jerk or shock; we were sitting side by side in a strange room. I looked round me. The walls were stone, limestone I think, rather roughly finished; mostly covered with cloth hangings. Tapestries: medieval, or imitation medieval. Very beautiful: maidens and knights and springtime gardens, flowers and graceful hounds and a sense of wonder. A high window let in pleasant muted light through what looked like waxed paper, or some sort of translucent animal skin. We were sitting on extremely real chairs, wooden, heavy, solid, hard.

—Where is this? I said.

—The twelfth century, I'm afraid, said Manny. Try not to worry too much.

I turned to look at him. He was wearing a long black robe. I tried not to worry too much.

We waited. One part of me was furious: William Morris fantasies are not my idea of socialism. But the shock and joy of seeing, of being with my friend and comrade, albeit in fancy dress; the continuing presence of pain, my other comrade; and a general sense of 'what the hell?'—all these kept it under control. Somewhat.

A heavy wooden door opened, and in came a woman. Manny stood up, respectfully, and put a calming hand on my shoulder to prevent my instinctive attempt to do the same.

She came towards us, took both Manny's hands in hers, smiled deeply, kindly.

—Jack, said Manny, this is Beatritz. She has some things to tell you.

I bowed my head towards her, awkwardly, and she smiled at me. She was older than me, in her late twenties, with a mass of deeply red hair held back with a simple band. She had astonishing eyes: blue, piercing, luminous, kind. She had—a kind of amused wisdom. She was beautiful.

With no preliminaries, she spoke.

—Your world is changing, Jack Tattersall, for the worse and then for the better; changing more than you can possibly imagine.

—For the better? I said; that's hard to believe.

—Give it time. You will see. Civilisation will survive the war that is about to start. Just. And then, gradually, the world will start to better itself. You will see it. It won't happen in the way that you imagine, or wish, but it will be better. It will be a fortunate time to be alive, at least where you will live; perhaps the best time for most people in the whole of the world's history, in many ways: material ways.

—That is wonderful, I said.

Yes, it is; but the amount of suffering will remain roughly the same.

—How can that be? I have offered my life to making that world, that material betterment, possible.

—You were right to do so. But in itself it is not enough. Believe me.

—How can I believe you? This is my life, my struggle, I will never abandon it, my friends have died for it, how can I trust anything you say? This is madness, and I am mad to take part in this conversation.

—I am not asking you to stop being a socialist; on the contrary. But what is important, Jack Tattersall, is this.

Her face changed. Became inward, calm, utterly composed. As if she withdrew, but at the same time became intensely present. A smile, a radiance, a sense of power and comfort. From this position, this assurance, she looked at me, the smile increasing, and I found myself smiling too: in fact, I was suffused with joy, I could feel it spreading through me, like a sunrise, a gift, a promise, a certainty. Only this mattered; yes, she was right.

What was it? What was it? You could call it love, but it was not that, or not any notion of love that I had ever experienced or dreamed: bliss, exaltation, peace, a dropping of the confines of the mind, like a warm bath, a cool drink, a solved problem, an answer, an end to pain.

I have never known such happiness. My eyes had closed, I was smiling, I was nowhere and everywhere. From a distance, I heard her voice.

—Remember this, Jack Tattersall, remember. Write it down. Write it for the daughter that you will one day have, she will need it. After you die, she will need it; write it, keep it safe, do not speak of it casually, this is for you and for her. Now go into the world and do good, from this gift that I have given you: be a good socialist, Jack, a good comrade, a good father and husband; but let that goodness arise naturally from this place that is beyond definition, beyond labels, that cannot be tied down.

Slowly, still in that happiness, I opened my eyes, and found I was back in the hospital grounds.

Hattie, Joel

You knew

—You knew didn't you?

—Yes, *meine freundin.* Yes.

—You have always known, haven't you?

—Yes.

—An end to pain. He called it an end to pain.

—Yes.

—Beyond—

—Yes.

—And now?

—Yes.

—No, I mean, what do I do now?

—Why are you asking, *liebchen*? Why?

—I don't know. Lingering self-doubt, I suppose.

—The last lament of an ego losing its footing. Cut the rope, Hattie. Cut the rope.

—Oh, Joel.

Rinchen, Hattie

Can I sit with you?

—Can I sit with you, Mum?

—Of course, dear. Of course.

—The Following Cat is coming too.

—Of course he is.

—Are we doing a practice?

—Not just now. Right now, we are just sitting.

—Actually, Mum, we're not doing anything. Sitting is happening.

—Did Rinpoche teach you to say it that way?

—Yes. But actually he just reminded me.

—Reminded you?

—Yes. He re-minded me. That's what he does.

—Thank you, precious. Thank you for re-minding me.

—You're welcome. Obviously. At least you would be, if—

—If what, Rinchen?

—If there were a me separate from a you to thank and a me separate from you to say you're welcome to.

—How about we do make believe thank you?

—Cool. I make believe you're welcome. Hey!

Charlie, Hattie

Well on my way

—Hattie. You look well. Really well.

—Thank you, dear. How are you?

—Coming through. On my way. Well on my way.

—Good. Then we can be well together.

—We are good together, aren't we? All of us I mean?

—All of us?

—You, me, Rinchen, Murray, the Following Cat—

—And?

—Yes. And Joel. You've taught me that.

—Charlie—

—Yes?

—I read some letters from my father yesterday. Beautiful letters. Important letters.

—Oh Hattie—my love—I'm so pleased. Is that what's been troubling you? I haven't helped you. I haven't been paying attention. Oh Hattie. I'm so sorry. So very sorry. You said you needed a hand—

—Cry if you can Charlie. I'm fine. I'm really happy. Cry if you can. It will help you be well.

Hattie: letter

Dear Margaret

Dear Margaret,

I am so very sorry to hear that Morris has died. I know just how good a man he was, and how much you meant to each other. My daughter, in her wisdom, called him Mr Greatheart. And I know she was not the only one to think of him that way. I am so very sad for the pain you must be feeling right now. What a terrible loss for you. For the family. For the community of friends that adored him and whom he adored. But most of all for you.

One day, when the time is right, and if you would like to, please come and stay here. Just now I know there is nothing I can say or do that would alleviate your distress. Nor should I. There is a wisdom in sorrow. In grief. In acknowledging fully and truthfully such a loss. But I have been given some precious gifts in this lifetime. Gifts of understanding that go way beyond any words I could write to you now. When the time is right, and if you care to, come and stay with us here. You will be most welcome.

Stay in touch.

We all send love.

Hattie Tattersall

September 2004

Rinchen: blog

Hattie's song

When I woke up this morning, I heard this strange high sound coming from downstairs. I thought maybe it was someone being sad again, so me and the Following Cat we went to check it out. The closer we got to it, the more we knew it was OK and only sad on the outside. The envelope. We tiptoed into the music room and there was Mum talking to someone we couldn't see but was probably Grandad because there was a Grandad feel to the room. At least that's what I thought and the Following Cat didn't disagree at all. Mum stopped speaking and went to the piano and started singing this really really beautiful song. Her singing it before was what had woken us up. It was different from any other song I've heard her sing ever and I've heard lots and lots. It was sad and not sad. Hurting and not hurting. With weird words and a tune that didn't make as much sense as usual. It made me think of Annabel's Mum's Jewish wedding music that she plays on her clarinet for us sometimes and we dance and clap. Only this song wasn't a dancing song. And it was no way a clapping song. It was a listening to the sound of the wind in the leaves of the trees song. We liked it.

Rinchen, Hattie

Sure as I can be

—What was that song Mum? The early morning sad and not sad song?

—Did you like it darling?

—Utterly. Yes. Will you sing it again for me, please?

—Yes, but not right now.

—Because?

—Because it's a wait-for-the-right-moment song.

—Yes. Obviously. Did you write it?

—Not really. The melody just played itself from somewhere—somewhere I don't think I've been. The words are from a famous play. Almost.

—Has Charlie been in it?

—Yes, actually. He'll tell you all about it when he's better.

—He will be better now, won't he?

—I'm pretty sure he will. Yes. I'm as sure as I can be.

—And that's really sure, isn't it, Mum? You know how to do sure, don't you?

—Yes. Yes, I think I do.

—So can I hear the song now, please?

—Sure.

Hattie: song

Full fathom five

full fathom five, my father lies
full fathom five
full fathom five
full fathom five
he
lies

those are pearls that were his eyes
(those are pearls that were his eyes)
nothing of him that doth fade
nothing of him that doth fade
but does suffer
a sea
change
into something rich and strange
in—to

some—thing
rich and
strange
into—something—rich—and—strange

Rinchen, Charlie

Interval

—Hey Charlie.

—Hey, hey, Rinchen.

—Are you busy writing again?

—It's a pause, actually.

—May I interrupt your pause?

—No interruption my sweet friend—an interlude.

—Is that like an interval—in a play?

—More or less. Yes.

—That's what I need to talk to you about, actually, Charlie.

—What is that precisely, dear heart?

—A play.

—Oh good. A new play? An old play?

—A play that has a song in it—the something rich and strange song.

—Ah, *that* play!

—Mum says you'll tell me about it when you're better. She says it's a good story.

—Shall we read it together, Rinchen? It's by the best.

—That Shakespeare person?

—Just so.

—It isn't a just so story is it?

—In a way.

—OK. When shall we read it together, Charlie? Can it be soon, please?

—It can be now if you like.

—I do like. I do. Does that mean you're better now, then?

—I think perhaps it does.

Rinchen, Joel

A bit confused

—Hey, Mr Joel.

—Hello, *kinderlach*.

—I think Charlie's getting better now.

—I think he is.

—We read a play by the Shakespeare person this afternoon and it was rich and strange.

—It is, isn't it.

—Do you know it, Joel?

—Yes, dear. Yes I do.

—I got a bit confused in places, but Charlie stopped and explained things.

—And do you understand it now?

—Well, actually I'm still a bit confused.

—Can I help you at all, *kinderlach*?

—No thank you, Joel. I think I'll stay a bit confused for a while. It's only a play. It's only a story in nice words. It's not real.

—I think you're less confused than you think you are, *kinderlach*.

Hattie, Charlie

Looking for a book

—Hello, dear.

—Hello, Hattie.

—Can I help?

—I'm looking for that book I sent Rinchen for her last birthday but one.

—Which book is that, then? I have a feeling you sent her at least a dozen. Or was that the roses? Or the conjuring tricks?

—Well—birthdays are important. Don't want the dear child to feel neglected.

—Oh Charlie—I'm so glad you're getting better.

—Me too. Hattie. I'm sorry I've—

—Don't you dare!

—I won't.

—Now then—which book?

—It was a big book of stories from plays of the Bard. Brightly coloured paintings. Unusually well done for a children's book.

—Oh, I know where it is—follow me. Is it for you or for her?

—For us both. We read *The Tempest* together today, and I may have confused her somewhat.

—You didn't try and tell her the Garamond story at the same time, did you?

—Well, no—but I couldn't resist a bit of digression here and there. Actors' tales—that sort of thing. The essentials of the plot got somewhat misty—distorted by improv parentheticals. I think it's my Godfatherly duty to set the record straight.

—Charlie, I think you're being too serious, darling. Way too serious. She'll sort it out.

—You think so? Really?

—Remember the Elvis Presley interlude? Birmingham Rep *Twelfth Night?*

—Should I feel guilty about that?

—Why do you ask?

—Self-doubt still looms, I'm afraid.

—Charlie. That's enough. This is a self-doubt-free zone.

—I was rather brilliant, as a matter of fact. Elvis, *c'est moi.*

—There you go.

—There I go.

Rinchen, Murray

Interesting

—Murray?

—Sweetheart?

—Guess what?

—Erm—no, you tell me.

—I heard Mum tell Charlie and then Joel that Ariel is coming to stay.

—That'll be interesting.

—Interesting? I'm a bit confused here, Murray.

—Can I help you, precious?

—I'm not sure Murray. I'll let you know.

—Right you are, precious.

Hattie: letter

Come and stay

2 September 2004

Dear Ariel,

Good to hear from you. I'm so pleased you are able to come and stay next weekend. Charlie is here, in recovery from a breakdown—doing well now and, though not his old self, busy introspecting and writing all about it, in a healthy way, and constructing a new one. I am so looking forward to seeing you again—it's been far too long to have been out of touch. You were such an inspiration to me and Charlie and Joel.

Since you ask, here's what was happening. Thank you for asking so directly. It feels correct to fill you in on some details of my life—what Charlie has started to call 'Hattie Tattersall: the Missing Years'. I've decided to write it up as a little prose piece so as to clarify information, and hopefully lay to rest some troubled times. I've been hiding this material away from people, and now it feels sensible not to do that anymore. Rest assured, the pain of it has lessened, and seems looser with each telling. Each admission of the past seems to bring a fresh level of acceptance.

We're looking forward to hearing your reactions to the filmscript that's not really a filmscript anymore, and would truly value your insights and suggestions about how to shape it now. We have yet to write the final scenes. That's going to take a courage I'm not sure we have yet. But we will finish it. We must now. I'm hopeful it will be soon.

My friend Murray will collect you from Henley station at 4.15 on Friday. Look for a gorgeous, extremely big man with long hair and a beard and a welcoming smile.

Charlie sends love along with mine—see you Friday.

Hattie.

Hattie: letter

Hattie Tattersall: the Missing Years.

In 1974, after Joel left, Charlie and I put all our energy into the band. It felt good to be doing that. We were looking after each other, and wrote and performed songs that made sense of what had happened—the deep love and friendship between the three of us—the immediate past—and (though people didn't know this, of course) our sense of a shared past in the twelfth century. Initially we did some other work too. I made that programme, but they didn't broadcast it—it was too way out for the times. Charlie did a little acting and directing—when things arose that interested him—and continued the work with the children in the hospital. He is so good with children.

Then, when Crazy Wisdom Lady really took off, we dropped everything else and put our energies into it completely. We had a marvellous support team, and eventually found the right drummer, and a lead guitarist that didn't make us think of Joel. Various other people joined us here and there—and, by the late seventies, we had that distinctive sound, a steady following; out of the pop mainstream of course—a folk rock sound that wasn't folk and wasn't rock. We went on tour after tour after tour. It was good fun in its way, and the songs were really classy. It had meaning. And it kept Charlie and me from thinking or feeling too much.

Then, in 1986, something in me broke. Exhaustion maybe. Too many places, too much travelling, too many stimulants. I got sick. Really sick. Couldn't perform. Couldn't even get out of bed. They called it M.E. and

I quickly spiralled downwards with depression and anxiety. We needed to close the band formally. The others needed work, and Charlie needed to do something creative. He was given some fantastic offers in the States—part directing, part lecturing—and off he went.

And me?

Orthodox medicine had nothing to offer apart from medication with weird side effects. I tried every self-help book, every alternative therapist going. Somehow, even through all the illness and exhaustion, some bit of me didn't give up. But nothing made much difference.

I was living at the time with Mark, the sound engineer who was working with us in the final year of *Crazy Wisdom Lady*: a beautiful sensitive man: an artist with sound. It was going well. We decided to have a baby. It was a foolish idea I suppose. We both knew I wasn't strong enough. But we went ahead, the way people do. Pregnancy was a cheering prospect at first. Hopeful. But then I miscarried. I wasn't prepared for what I saw when the baby came out of me—tiny hands—I'll never forget those hands. But I sank back into exhaustion, and didn't feel much really. Mark tried to be supportive. But our relationship wasn't strong enough to see this through. Not his fault. A good man. A kind and interesting man. But not Joel. Not Charlie. Not his fault.

Then, in 1989, February it was, just after all of this, Mum died. Suddenly. Her heart. She'd been poorly for a while, but it was unexpected. Dad couldn't cope. He had no frame of reference for dealing with this. This domestic tragedy. This loss of his life-long companion. He was angry. As I watched him, unable to take it in, unable to grieve, I saw myself. We had understood the big picture so well—me and Joel and Charlie—that simple human emotions had gone unnoticed. One day, in a traffic jam. I started to cry. And I cried for weeks.

I don't remember that summer too well. I know it was summer. But the details of it are fuzzy. I cried. I slept deeply. I had strange dreams. People came to look after me. People stayed. People left. Other people stayed. I was in a world of my own. I'm sorry now that I wasn't properly available for Dad at the time. He was throwing himself into local politics. Not coping with world changes. Not coping without Mum being there.

I do remember a huge row we had. I was finding my feet again. He must have been worried about me, but it came out as an explosion. Stuff he'd been bottling up. I had found a meditation teacher and he didn't like it. I think he felt he'd lost me, as well as everything else. But in a funny sort of way, the argument did us good—woke us both up. What were we doing to each other? Our love had always been rock solid—whatever our differing opinions. I persuaded him to come and stay for a while. We talked properly for the first time in ages. I wanted him to leave politics and come and live with me. But of course he wouldn't. And that was fine too. I knew he wanted to be where he felt he belonged. But we stayed in very close touch after that. We laughed together again, got excited by big ideas, and had good-hearted arguments about all of it. And, thank goodness, he at last let me give him some money.

His death, this April, turned my world upside down. I won't write about it here, Ariel. It's still too recent, too raw, too vast in its effects and implications for this tidy little piece of prose. We will tell you the whole, exquisite story when you're here with us. It will take time, and delicacy and I look forward to it, because you will be the best of listeners. You were there for us thirty years ago. It's strangely fitting that you should be here for the weaving together of these fine threads of narrative and meaning.

I started to write songs again. To perform every now and then, if I felt like it. Started painting too—huge, wild canvases. I found the perfect spiritual teacher—a Tibetan Lama with enough wildness in him to understand mine, and a good humoured kindness that encouraged me to balance the crazy wisdom with a steadier, more disciplined set of practices, so that I could sort my mind out. He stayed here for a while too. He went to the States in '97 and teaches now in Boulder, Colorado. We talk on the phone regularly, and email each other. He visits when he comes to Europe. He gave me so much to be grateful for. Even before he brought me my beautiful adopted daughter.

Rinchen is her name. Tiny, exquisite, wise. Rinpoche had been to visit his family in Tibet and had come out of a special retreat in the mountains to carry her to freedom himself—escaping over the vast, inhospitable mountains from the Chinese. Her parents died early on in the journey. Rinpoche told me to go to India and bring her home here. So I did. There were formalities to go through, of course. I employed good lawyers. Sensitive people.

And here we are.

I live in this beautiful big house with its graceful English gardens. My gorgeous daughter is now nearly ten years old. Charlie agreed to be her non-Godfather. And, importantly, her legal guardian should anything happen to me. He takes this role seriously. If anything at all could have strengthened our amazing friendship—then this is it. Rinchen is still her deep, inner name, but when she was coming up to her fourth birthday, and Charlie asked her what she wanted for a birthday present, she said she wanted to be called Charlie too. So, of course, he gave her his name—on the understanding that they needed to share it. We have been putting her down on paper as Charlotte when there are schools, doctors and form-fillers to please. But she insisted for years that her name was Charly. When big Charlie was ill, and lost inside himself, last winter, she gave the name back to him, so as not to confuse him. Currently she's Rinchen all the time. We'll see what she chooses as she grows up. Knowing my gorgeous daughter, she'll probably use both names so as to keep people on their toes. Remind me to tell you about the Gingerbread Pig, when you're here. She is a constant delight and source of amazement and wonder. Being with her is complete happiness. And I find myself re-connecting with the inner peace I knew when I first met Joel and Charlie. There is a certainty in things again. I know who I am and what I'm doing.

There is a sense of, somehow, having come full circle now. And a need for big Charlie and me to re-connect deeply, more deeply than ever before, to remember, and to discover something new—or, more accurately, to rediscover something we once knew and have forgotten.

Rinchen, Murray

Big magician person

—Hello, Murray.

—Hello, Petal.

—Am I a flower?

—You're a precious petal, Petal.

—OK. Do you know Mum's special guest who's coming this weekend?

—Not yet. Do you know her?'

—I know about her. She's been living on an island. Making up stories.

—Has she? I lived on an island once.

—You've been all sorts of strange places Murray.

—Yes, I have, Petal.

—But you're here now, aren't you?

—For the duration, my flower. Yes I'm well and truly here.

—Is duration like endurance Murray?

—I suppose it is.

—Is that good or bad?

—Not good not bad.

—Just is?

—Just necessary.

—Just essential?

—Just so.

—Will you cook something special for the visitor?

—What do you think she'd like?

—I'm not sure at all Murray. She's been working for a big magician person on the island.

—Has she? Is she in show business?

—I'll ask Charlie. He told me the story.

Rinchen, Charlie

Good serious

—Hey, Charlie.

—Hey hey, Rinchen.

—Can I ask you a question?

—All yours, sweetheart.

—Is Ariel in show business?

—She was.

—When?

—When she used to teach us—me, Hattie, Joel—when we were students together.

—Did she do magic tricks?

—In a way she did. We thought she was magical.

—You don't mean rabbits out of hats here, do you, Charlie?

—No. She made ideas come alive.

—Really? How did she do that?

—By caring passionately about them. By speaking in poetry about them. By sharing her dreams. By inspiring everyone who was listening to care as much as she did.

—And was everyone listening?

—Not everyone. But some. Enough, maybe.

—And is that show business?

—No, perhaps not. There was a whole lot of show business going on, but she was our teacher. Serious.

—Good serious?

—Definitely.

—Like Rinpoche?

—No. I don't think so. No, probably not like Rinpoche, really.

—In what way same and in what way different, please, Charlie?

—Maybe you should ask Hattie.

—OK.

Rinchen, Hattie

Knowing the island

—Charlie says to ask you something.

—For him or for you?

—For me first, then I'll go and tell him too, I expect.

—OK. Ask whatever you want, darling.

—Well, it's concerning Ariel.

—Concerning is good. Where did you learn that?

—I saw it on a typed letter on your desk and asked Murray about it because I thought it might mean that someone was concerned but he explained it meant they weren't at all concerned and told me how to use it this way. As a sort of RE:

—OK. I understand. So, concerning Ariel?

—Well Charlie says she was your teacher but not like Rinpoche.

—That's right.

—So what's the same and what's different please?

—That's a good question, sweetheart. I'm not sure I know the answer precisely.

—Fuzzy will do, Mum.

—OK—fuzzy it may be. Ariel is kind like Rinpoche and knows a lot like he does and inspires people like he does. And, in a way, she takes them way beyond what they were expecting to learn, like he does.

—Does she help them like he does?

—Actually she does—or did when we knew her well. Yes. She was good at helping people. Especially she would help them trust themselves—their own knowing.

—So why is she different?

—Well, really, she's not much different. It's more a question of who has taught her and what she has studied, and the places she's explored.

—You mean the inside places, don't you, Mum?

—Yes I do, darling.

—OK, I'm beginning to get it. Is it like she knows a little and Rinpoche knows lots?

—It's more like Ariel knows the island in all its strangeness and wonder, and the sea around it and the sky too maybe, but Rinpoche knows the whole world and its place in the galaxies and then many other worlds besides. Worlds that we can only dream of.

—I think Ariel should meet Rinpoche.

—That's a good idea. Why don't you tell her that when she comes to stay?

Rinchen, Joel

Practising for Charlie

—Hey, Mr Joel. Long time no see.

—Hey hey, *wunderkind.*

—Did you know that Ariel is coming to stay? Tomorrow.

—And tomorrow and tomorrow?

—Yes, the whole weekend.

—Good.

—Will you be here too?

—Yes. It's been a long time since we met. She was very kind to me.

—Was she?

—Very.

—I'm a bit confused here, Joel.

—Aren't we all?

—You sound like present Charlie. Has he called yet?

—No, not yet. I'm still perfecting voices for when he does though. Tell me more about your confusion.

—Well you say she was kind, but Charlie says she made waves.

—Yes, she did.

—Big storms.

—You could stay that. She was a radical thinker. A brilliant teacher.

—Did you get wet?

—In a manner of speaking. Yes.

—I think it's the manner of speaking that's confusing me, Joel.

—I'm sorry, Rinchen. I've been practising too much for Charlie.

—Well please stop for a bit now.

—I will. I promise. Give me a moment.

Rinchen, Ariel

Curly clouds

—Hello Ariel, I'm Rinchen.

—Hello Rinchen, I'm pleased to meet you.

—Me too. This is the Following Cat.

—I'm pleased to meet you too.

—Are you comfortable?

—I'm extremely comfortable, thank you.

—Did you fly back from the island?

—Yes, I did.

—Did you ride on the curly clouds?

—Well now—how did you know that?

—Charlie's told me all about you.

—All hail, dear sister! Rinchen, hail! I come
To answer thy best pleasure; be't to fly,
To swim, to dive into the fire, to ride
On the curl'd clouds, to thy strong bidding task
Ariel and all her quality.

—Cool! Can you magic previous Charlie back please? Only more so?'

Rinchen, Murray

Shape shifter

—I like Ariel, Murray.

—Yes. Me too.

—You'd never know she was a shape-shifter, would you?

—Is she?

—That's what Charlie said when he was telling me the story.

—Well, I'm privileged to be cooking for a shape-shifter.

—I'm glad you aren't one, Murray.

—I'm glad you're glad, Flower. Why so glad?

—You can have too much shape-shifting sometimes I think, Murray. It's nice you stay solid and same.

—There's a lot to be said for shape-shifting though, don't you think?

—Maybe. Depends on the shape, I think.

—Say more, Flower.

—Well, obviously when Rinpoche changes into Chenrezig or Medicine Buddha or one of the pretend scary ones it's totally cool, because he really really knows how to do that. And you know he's doing it for the benefit of all beings. So it's even more totally cool.

—Cool beyond cool, I would say.

—Me too. And, actually, when previous Charlie used to turn into the big clown or Sir John the famous actor or that Cosmo person or a zillion other makebelieve people, that was pretty cool too.

—I can hear a 'but' coming up, Flower.

—Yes, there is a but.

—And what is it?

—I don't like it that he's a different shape now, Murray. I don't like it that Grandad's a different shape.

—I can understand that completely, my friend. Would you like a hug from yours truly?

—Mine sincerely?

—Absolutely.

—Yes please, Murray. A solid hug please. Solid and same.

Rinchen, Ariel

Free from the story

—Ariel, are you free now?

—I certainly am free to have a cup of tea with you, Rinchen.

—Here you are. It's green tea.

—Perfect, thank you.

—You're welcome. But I mean are you really free?

—Well, I have another month before I start working at the University again, but that's not what you mean, is it?

—No, it isn't.

—Well, I'm listening, Rinchen. Ask whatever you want to.

—I mean are you free from the story?

—The story?

—Yes. The story. The magic power person? The man with the books.

—The man with the books? What do you think?

—Well, excuse me for saying so, but I don't think you are quite. I hope you don't think that's a rude thing to say?

—No, I'm fascinated. Thank you for your concern. Why do you think I'm not free?

—Because you talk about books all the time. And because you have books books books by you when you sleep. And because there's more of you in your head than in the rest of you. I do hope you don't think that's a rude thing to say also?

—No. I'm still very fascinated Rinchen. How do you think I might get free?

—I think you should come and meet Rinpoche when he comes here to teach next time. He knows lots and plenty that you don't get from books.

—And when is he coming, do you know?

—Yes, I do, actually. After summer.

—Merrily?

—Merrily.

—Shall I live now?

—Obviously.

—I'll be here, Rinchen. I am truly interested in being free. Obviously.

Hattie: letter

We've done it

23 September 2004

Dear Ariel,

Well, we've done it. Thank you so much for your help and encouragement. You are a joy and an inspiration as always. I enclose the final scenes for you to enjoy. I think we've got them as they need to be. It was, as you predicted, an extraordinarily therapeutic thing to do—once we'd acknowledged just how painful it was bound to be—well, we just sat up all night on the day you left us, and just started and didn't stop till we were through to the end.

We'll be in touch again soon. We're really looking forward to reading your novel-that-isn't-quite-a-novel whenever you're ready to share it. And I'll let you know the exact dates for Rinpoche's visit as soon as we have them.

Love from us all here. I'm so glad you were able to see Joel whilst you were here, and happy for him that he could drop by and re-connect with you. You were such a significant catalyst in his life; in all our lives. Rinchen thought you were awesome, by the way, and was much impressed by your sensitivity to Ayesha and the Following Cat. She particularly loved it that you spoke poetry to them, knowing they would understand.

Rinchen still thinks that you are somehow Shakespeare's Ariel, and we can't persuade her otherwise. Enjoy the freedom of the Island!

With much love

Hattie

Hattie, Charlie: filmscript 29

Summer holiday

INT. CHARLIE'S HOUSE: MUSIC ROOM—MORNING

April 1974.

HATTIE is looking at maps. JOEL and CHARLIE are tinkering with music.

HATTIE
Quéribus. What a name.

JOEL
What is it?

HATTIE
I don't know, I just know I've got to go there. I just know it.

HATTIE reaches for green Michelin—looks it up.

HATTIE (CONT'D)
Ah, right, that's why. It's a castle, a derelict castle.

CHARLIE
Are you still on the Toulouse map?

HATTIE
Yes, the big one: *(paraphrasing from Michelin)* it's 150 miles from Toulouse.

It's one of the main Cathar refuges from the crusade. Some of the Cathars who escaped from Montségur stayed there on the way to Spain. It's special: I know it is. I'm going to go there. Do you want to come too?

JOEL and CHARLIE put their instruments down, and come and look at maps.

CHARLIE
Yes, fantastic, haven't had a holiday for ages. We can go down in the bus, rent a gîte, hang out together.

JOEL
That would make a nice change.

CHARLIE
Yes, wouldn't it. Hey, look, it's really mountainous round there—we can take the climbing gear and get some serious climbing in.

JOEL
Is that OK with you, Hattie?

HATTIE
It'll be great, I'll need some time and space to myself, to be quiet and feel the feelings of the place. This is the heartland, you know. This is where they lived and died. I want to get back to that Toulouse experience. I want to breathe the air.

JOEL
I want to eat the food.

CHARLIE
Darling, the cheese… *(stagey voice)*

JOEL
Yes, dear. I'll peel the onions.

CHARLIE

Well you'll have to darling, or my make-up will simply disintegrate. And you know how merciless the cameras are.

JOEL

And one's reputation is just utterly lost.

HATTIE

OK darlings, let's plan this properly. Joel, darling, do you by any chance have some food you might have already prepared?

JOEL

Say no more. You are about to be amazed.

He leaves room to go to kitchen. He reappears with huge meal - stupendous dish, elaborate salad, fresh bread, three forks.

They begin studying the maps—getting excited.

JOEL (CONT'D)

Oms. We have to stay in Oms. Not om, Oms: more is better.

MONTAGE: THE FRENCH HOLIDAY

--*Packing up van in England.*

--*Travelling down French road with trees, springtime but cold.*

--*Sitting by river eating bread and wine and cheese.*

--*Bouncing along in van, singing. Poring over map.*

--*Sitting in café: a man wearing a yarmulke comes over to* JOEL

MAN

Sorry to hear about your death.

--*Arriving in the mountains.*

EXT. QUÉRIBUS—MORNING

Castle ruins. In the castle, at the top of the mountain, looking at the Pyrenees. HATTIE *stays in castle, just looking at mountains.* JOEL *and* CHARLIE *scramble round, explore, then come back. Springtime, early, quite cold but very sunny, wrapped up in warm clothing; snow on distant mountains. Medieval music.*

CAMERA ON FACES—EMPHASISING LIGHT AND SHADE.

HATTIE

This is perfect.

CHARLIE
Parfait.

HATTIE
Thank you so much for coming here with me. This means a lot. This is the source: here, in this spot. This exact spot. I have never been happier.

Sunlight through the window. Light and shade—suggestion of 12c alter egos showing through—understated.

JOEL
Just being here, together, the three of us, is enough. It is what we came for.

CHARLIE
To France?

JOEL
No.

Charlie nods. Full sunlight on his face—radiance.

INT. GÎTE IN OMS—MORNING

HATTIE, JOEL, and CHARLIE are sitting on a rug in front of the fire. There is a lumpy old sofa in the background, big pot of coffee, breadboard, butter, jam, cheese: late breakfast. Sunlight coming through the window.

HATTIE
I want to stay here: I need to be quiet and think.

CHARLIE
Those mountains we could see from Quéribus—*(to JOEL)* let's take the climbing gear and go and have a look at them.

JOEL
Yes, there's a pull, isn't there? Something about those peaks.

CHARLIE
(To HATTIE—he is reading the map) That's quite a substantial drive, particularly in the mountains. Is it OK with you if we start really early tomorrow, and stay a night in the bus, and come back late the night after that?

HATTIE
Yes, there's plenty of food and wine here. If you're lucky I'll have a nice meal waiting for you when you get back, but don't count on it because I'm writing songs and may forget the time.

CHARLIE

We know you're all right for supplies, but *(in a deliberately childlike voice)* won't you miss us?

HATTIE

That's one of the songs. I'll play it to you later.

INT. GÎTE IN OMS: LIVING ROOM—NIGHT

*By the fireside that night—*HATTIE, JOEL, *and* CHARLIE *are drinking wine, having eaten.*

HATTIE *sings the song 'Go in Peace'. In her guitar accompaniment, it has one minor chord, when she sings "but go" for the first time.*

> when sunshine dazzles, I would shelter you
> when twilight hovers, I would comfort you
> I'd be the light when darkness falls
> when morning beckons, I would borrow you
>
> when summer maddens, I'd be calm for you
> when autumn mists come, I'd be clear for you
> I'd be the warmth when winter calls
> when springtime rushes, I'd be still for you
>
> holding you close to me
> keeping you safe with me
> knowing that you have to
> go now
>
> watching you watching me
> loving you loving me
> knowing it's time for you to
> go now
>
> so go well
> go in peace
> *but go*
>
> so go well
> go in peace
> but go

CHARLIE *and* JOEL *are silent.*

CHARLIE

(Gently humorous) One sad note, is that all we get?

HATTIE

(Seriously—more seriously than at any other point in the movie) Just one sad note.

*Suddenly she laughs her notorious laugh—*CHARLIE *and* JOEL *join in— everything is fine.*

Hattie, Charlie: Filmscript 30

Inquisition

INT. CASTLE: BEATRITZ' MUSIC ROOM—AFTERNOON

BEATRITZ

The Inquisition will be here tomorrow. They want you above all others— you know that, don't you?

PARFAIT

Yes, I know that.

BEATRITZ

What will you do?

PARFAIT

When the Inquisition comes, there will be deaths. Perhaps many deaths. Some of those who will die are not yet consoled. I must stay and find some way of consoling them.

BEATRITZ

Then you must disguise yourself: it is you they want.

PARFAIT

Yes. *(Reluctantly)* Yes. It is necessary.

BEATRITZ

My friend the Troubadour will help you. He knows the taverns where you will not be recognised. He moves freely through town and country; he mixes with everyone. He will know what to do.

INT. CASTLE: BEATRITZ' MUSIC ROOM—NIGHT

The PARFAIT *seems to be alone in the room—he is taking off his black robe and putting on clothes that we recognize as clothes that the* TROUBADOUR *wears. Before he undresses he carefully tears one black thread from his robe. He takes off the robe and binds the thread round his upper arm. Then he puts on a colourful jacket. Camera pulls back and we see that the* TROUBADOUR *is looking on.*

MONTAGE: THE PARFAIT AND TROUBADOUR GETTING TO KNOW ONE ANOTHER

The two men, walking, eating, sitting by a river, talking and talking, intense conversations, laughter, TROUBADOUR *plays lute in one scene,* PARFAIT *listens. Summer turning into autumn.*

INT. CASTLE DINING ROOM, NOW A MAKESHIFT COURT—AFTERNOON

BEATRITZ *in plain black shift.* MONK *writing down everything said.* INQUISITOR *in monk's robe.*

Slow pace. Languorous. Boring. A buzzing fly; a scribe writing everything down with a scratchy pen. Full of menace.

INQUISITOR

Lady, in the last two months we have talked to many of your servants.

BEATRITZ

Yes. I have tended the wounds of those conversations.

INQUISITOR

Their souls are cleaner for our visit.

BEATRITZ *looks at him with contempt.*

INQUISITOR

We now know without doubt that you have had many conversations with the arch-heretic Guillaume de Loris, and we know that you have been with him to visit the dying, and have been doing the devil's work. Do you deny this?

BEATRITZ *is silent.*

INQUISITOR (CONT'D)

Your silence is itself damning. Now, we must proceed. We must find de Loris before he does more damage. The spiritual health of this region is in danger from him. We hear of him everywhere. He must be stopped. Do you know where he is to be found?

BEATRITZ *is silent.*

INQUISITOR (CONT'D)

If you do not tell us we will assume from your silence that you have been hereticated. And we will burn you.

BEATRITZ is silent.

INQUISITOR

In four days time we will place a stake in your courtyard. At dawn we will tie you to it and light the fire.

EXT. CASTLE COURTYARD—MORNING

It is the day after the inquisitor's threat to burn BEATRITZ. She is in the courtyard, which is very beautiful, sitting and thinking. Suggestions of guards in background. She is peaceful.

EXT. FRENCH COUNTRYSIDE—CONTINUOUS

Beside a stream. The PARFAIT is sitting in the same posture as BEATRITZ in the previous scene. He looks up alertly. Pause. He turns to the TROUBADOUR.

PARFAIT

It is time: I must go to the castle.

TROUBADOUR

I will come with you.

PARFAIT

No: they will burn you too. Be free.

TROUBADOUR

Go well: go in peace.

They embrace.

INT. CASTLE DINING ROOM, NOW A MAKESHIFT COURT—MORNING

PARFAIT

Will you now free her?

INQUISITOR

No. She has not repented. She has remained silent. She will burn.

The PARFAIT turns and looks at her.

INT. CASTLE: A CELL—NIGHT

It is the night after the Inquisition scene. The PARFAIT is in meditation.

INT. CASTLE: BEATRITZ' BEDROOM—CONTINUOUS

BEATRITZ is asleep. In her dream she receives the consolamentum *from the* PARFAIT *who appears to be at her bedside. They go joyfully into the fire. Afterwards, her blue eyes shine with the light of the spirit.*

EXT. CASTLE COURTYARD—MORNING

The fire of BEATRITZ'*s dream becomes the Inquisition's fire in the courtyard.* BEATRITZ *and the* PARFAIT *are in it. They are singing. We see her blue eyes. The song is the one that* JOEL *hears in his Provençal dream, 'Through the Fire to the Light', that he turns into the modern song for the band 'Through the Fire'. Shots of crowd, kneeling. Inquisitors and soldiers cross themselves and look fearful. Camera goes into flames and fade out.*

Hattie, Charlie: filmscript 31

Mountain

INT. PYRENEES: FOOT OF SCREE SLOPE: IN THE VAN—MORNING

The van parked at the foot of a scree slope. A clear spring day in the Pyrenees

CHARLIE

Just look at that—perfect. That ridge up there, that's where we're going.

JOEL

It's the perfect day—the perfect day. They don't come better than this.

EXT. PYRENEES: FOOT OF SCREE SLOPE—MORNING

Clear spring day—spectacular views. JOEL *and* CHARLIE *are getting kit together—putting on boots.*

CHARLIE

What did you bring for lunch?

JOEL

Wait and see, a special treat.

CHARLIE

Will I like it?

JOEL

Don't you always?

CHARLIE

(Laughs) I'm really glad we're doing this. It's part of it, somehow. Up there on the mountain, there is truth to be found—I know it.

JOEL

OK, but first we have to get up there.

EXT. PYRENEES: GOING UP THE MOUNTAIN—LATER

A series of scenes. Snatches of conversation.

JOEL

It's getting a bit exposed, we'd better rope up.

CHARLIE

Up that gully then, don't you think?

JOEL

Yes, OK.

CHARLIE

Careful of this bit, the snow's a little flaky.

EXT. PYRENEES: ON THE RIDGE—LATER

JOEL and CHARLIE are standing on mountain ridge after their climb up. They have clear view of Quéribus. Music that was playing for that scene is playing again here.

CHARLIE

That's Quéribus over there: spectacular place, isn't it?

JOEL

Strange how you can't tell whether it's far away or close at hand. I love the way perspective shifts when you're this high.

CHARLIE

OK, let's do the ridge—then that gully you can see going down on the left.

EXT. PYRENEES: ON THE RIDGE—LATER

CHARLIE and JOEL are walking in the snow, on a high ridge. Brilliant sunshine, blue sky. Loosely roped together, carrying loops of rope casually. They are kitted out with boots and anoraks and have ice axes. JOEL is leading.

Suddenly the snow gives way under JOEL. It's a cornice, and too thin, and the whole ledge of snow that he is standing on collapses and falls away, taking him with it. CHARLIE is still on stable snow, though attached to JOEL

by the rope; to stop himself from being pulled over the edge, he slams his
ice-axe into the snow and loops the rope round it twice before JOEL's full
weight can bring the rope taut. Shout of pain from JOEL. Bang, the rope
goes rigid. Establishing shots: from CHARLIE's point of view, the ice-axe,
the taut rope, the edge of a snow cliff, sky. JOEL has vanished. Then a shot
of JOEL: he is hanging from the rope, in mid-air, 5 metres down from the
overhanging edge, over a huge drop, nursing one arm with the other. Back
to CHARLIE's point of view: he is clinging to the other end of the rope which
is looped round the ice axe, which is embedded (but not firmly) in the snow.
Stillness, much tension. Heavy breath.*

CHARLIE

(Shouts) Joel, Joel, are you OK?

Silence.

CHARLIE

Joel? Joel? *(Voice breaking).*

*Flock of birds shoots out. JOEL has blacked out. CHARLIE considers the
position. The ice axe is not firm.*

JOEL

Charlie! Charlie!

CHARLIE

Oh thank God. How are you?

JOEL

I'm fine apart from my arm—which is broken. I'm a long way out from the
rock dangling free. And it's a long long way down. How's your belay?

CHARLIE

(Looks at ice axe) Fine. *(It's not fine. It's quite loose.)* Is there any chance
you can climb back up?

JOEL

Not with this arm: not a hope. Can you pull me up?

CHARLIE tries. The belay gets worse. Tries again. Belay gets worse.

CHARLIE

No, the belay won't take it.

JOEL

Charlie, tell me the absolute truth. How long will that belay hold both of us?

CHARLIE
Minutes.

JOEL
Charlie, do this for me. Cut the rope. If you don't, we're both dead. Do it for me.

CHARLIE
No. I'm ready to die. (*Quick flash of dream of going into the fire.*) I can handle it: I'm ready.

JOEL
It's not about you: it's about Hattie. Cut the rope.

CHARLIE
Sorry, can't do that. I just can't do it.

JOEL
OK then. I have a knife, thank God.

EXT. PYRENEES: ON THE RIDGE: UNDER THE CORNICE—CONTINUOUS

JOEL *hanging from rope. He pulls a knife out of his pocket and opens it with his teeth.*

CHARLIE
(*Shouts, voice breaking*) Joel, no!

JOEL
It's OK. it's really OK. This is why we came up the mountain. This is why we came to France. I can hear the song. It's in my blood. I love you both. Take care of each other.

Cuts rope. Black. Silence.

INT. GÎTE IN OMS—MORNING

HATTIE *sitting on the rug in front of the fire, which is burning, leaning against the lumpy old sofa. Guitar, pencil and paper to hand. She has a mirror in her hand.*

She is laughing and crying, holding the mirror; HATTIE *has had the same experience as* BEATRITZ *will have in the next scene.*

FLASHBACK

EXT. CASTLE GARDEN—MORNING

BEATRITZ *is in the garden—it is after she has witnessed the consolamentum. She has the death scene in mind. She holds up a small mirror, sunlight glances off mirror, she goes through the mirror into the white light. Comes out laughing and crying.*

BEATRITZ

It's so simple—so simple.

VOICE-OVER: PARFAIT/JOEL

Now you can see why we are not afraid.

FLASHBACK ENDS

HATTIE

It's so very simple.

INT. GÎTE IN OMS: VERANDAH—MORNING

HATTIE *is sitting on the verandah of the gîte. She is looking at the mountains where* CHARLIE *and* JOEL *are climbing. She falls into a light sleep.*

She dreams of the fire; sees LADY *and* PARFAIT *in flames, singing. As in earlier scene.*

PARFAIT (VOICE-OVER)

Some of us, and this is a deep secret, do not accept that the goal is to cease to incarnate; some of us choose, having received the transmission, to return nonetheless to this difficult place, because it is not acceptable to leave anyone behind in it.

Song 'Through the Fire' comes up strongly again.

HATTIE *wakes up—startled—looks up at the mountain. The song is being sung. She joins in singing it.*

EXT. GÎTE IN OMS: OUTSIDE—MORNING

Packing up to go back in the bus. Locking door, loading stuff into van; CHARLIE *is going to drive it back,* HATTIE *will fly back with the coffin.* CHARLIE *is devastated: he is as if in a dream.* HATTIE *is firm and practical.*

HATTIE

OK, before you go, listen to this. I found it last night. It's in Joel's handwriting—one of his Rumi translations. He was working on it on the way here, on the long, sweet journey here. This is our goodbye to him. Oh Charlie. This is his goodbye to us.

Reads poem.

HATTIE

> In the end you disappeared, gone beyond sight
> Strange, the path you took, leaving this world
> Strange how the beat of your wings destroyed the cage
> And you flew to the world of the soul.
>
> You were a nightingale, drunk amidst the owl music
> Drunk with the music of joy
> When the scent of the rose garden reached you
> You were gone.
>
> The bitter wine you drank with us has left us hung over
> While you went to drink beyond time
> Like an arrow you went towards bliss
> So straight, so sure of the target.
>
> This world tried to deceive you, with its evidence.
> You refused; you refused the false clues;
> You went straight to the place beyond certainty.
>
> Now that you are the sun, what good is a crown?
> And how do you tie your belt
> Now that your body is air?
>
> You were rain from heaven
> That fell on this dry earth
> And ran everywhere, everywhere
> You ran laughing down the gutter.
>
> Be silent. Be free
> Of all the pain of speech
> Don't sleep, since you have moved in
> With so wonderful a Lover.

They hug each other, weep.

INT. SMALL COUNTRY CHURCH IN ENGLAND—MORNING

Springtime in England. It's JOEL's funeral – conducted by the Vicar (JOHN) with whom he had become friends in the rare pig charity gig—sound of CHARLIE *and* HATTIE *singing 'Time after time'. Sung simply.*

The church is packed with people. We recognise CHARLIE'S MOTHER, GRAND-FATHER, ARIEL ANDREWS; *a lot of people: a lot of friends. The* SHOPKEEPER *from the Leeds Jewish delicatessen is there—out of place and uncomfortable and puzzled as to why* JOEL *is being buried in a church.*

Small mimed scene between HATTIE *and Jewish delicatessen man; she is explaining something—and indicates the silver pig necklace as she's talking. Aha! He understands why the funeral would be in an English country church—it's a Gingerbread Pig thing to do. He smiles and kisses Hattie gently on the cheek.*

Shots of the VICAR JOHN *conducting the ceremony.*

Coffin with JOEL'S *guitar on it.*

EXT. SMALL COUNTRY CHURCH IN ENGLAND: OUTSIDE—CONTINUOUS

Air view of country church. The music of CHARLIE *and* HATTIE'S *song, 'Time after Time', carries through—somehow we know that* CHARLIE *and* HATTIE *have the secret of the joyful death and they are very free. Rising up from the church; there is a skylark, the music blends.*

> time after time I will find you
> time after time there'll be tears and laughter
> time after time I'll remind you
> of this
> time after
> time after
> time after
> time
>
> like the warm summer rain
> falling softly from above
> you brought joy to meet the pain
> to a world thirsty for love
>
> like the nightingale in song
> calling softly through the night
> you found your way to belong
> in a world yearning for light

like the bird leaving its cage
you have flown on freedom's wing
you have left this shadow stage
for a place where truth will sing

like the arrow from its bow
you have flown to follow your bliss
you have left this passing show
for the soul's own waking kiss

know that
time after time I will find you
time after time there'll be tears and laughter
time after time I'll remind you
of this
time after
time after
time after
time

INT. MADISON SQUARE GARDENS—EVENING

Summer 1980. Madison Square Gardens, huge concert, big backing group: serious musicians, CHARLIE *mixed in with them,* HATTIE *piano and vocals, spotlight on her.*

They're singing the song 'Time after Time'. It carries on through from JOEL's *funeral. It's the same song—but with heavy rock arrangement.*

It's also the same concert that was a flash-forward the night the band was formed and named in CHARLIE's *music room.*

FADE OUT

Rinchen: blog

Good work

Well blog. We did good work today. It was farout and mad and totally in the groove. I'm going to tell you all about it because now it is a good warm feeling inside like hot chocolate in bed with your dressing gown on and the Following Cat waiting for you to snuggle down so he can settle down also and heavy on your legs. I hope you're listening carefully.

It started in the middle of the night. I got up to go and get a drink from the kitchen and I heard Mum and Charlie in the music room talking and typing on Charlie's laptop and it was so late it was nearly early maybe even morning not night because the birds were almost starting to sing. I looked in to see if maybe they would like me to be there too but they were writing and talking and typing and waving their arms about and didn't see me and there was a glow light all around them like one big fuzzy egg so I went back to bed. I listened for a bit and maybe heard some crying, but not bad crying so I didn't worry too much. Not too much.

In the morning, I spoke with Murray.

—Hello, Murray.

—Hello, Rinchen.

—Where is Mum?

—She's gone to the post office to post a parcel to Ariel.

—Why so early, Murray?

—I think she wanted to get something done and dusted, Damson.

—Am I a soft fruit today, Murray?

—Never sweeter, sweetheart.

—Thank you, Murray. And where is Charlie?

—I think he's in the garden.

—With anyone?

—With himself, I think.

So I went into the garden and saw Charlie in his crumpled blue clothes from yesterday sitting on a bench by the wall and not shaved or anything and limp like a puppet without strings attached and staring at nothing precisely. He was staring but not looking or watching or seeing or any of those things.

—Joel? Joel?

—Here I am, my special friend.

—I think Charlie's fire is on the way out again.

—I think you're right.

—What shall I do?

—You know what to do, *liebchen*. You know exactly what to do.

286

—This is true Joel. You sound like my Mum today. Will you stay here please?

—I'm here. Right here. Here like always.

—Thank you, Joel.

I went back into the kitchen.

—Murray?

—Rinchen?

—I've got a job to do.

—Can I help you?

—Yes please Murray. I think Charlie's fire is going out again and I have to go and make it not.

—I'm coming right away.

—Excuse me please Murray, but we need to do this extra special way.

—I'm with you there my friend. What's your plan?

—You will please come and stand close by Charlie but a bit away and say the Green Tara mantra and be there in case he needs a big strong person like yourself as well as a little person like me.

—And the Following Cat?

—No, this is no place for a cat. He will stay here and keep the kitchen nice.

—Got you. I'm right beside you all the way.

—Thank you, Murray.

So we went into the garden and Murray stood there like a huge angel without wings but glowing like a golden bird or maybe a tiger and very softly said the Green Tara mantra *om tare tuttare ture soha* over and over and very beautiful. And I stood in front of Charlie who was nearly not and got bigger and more solid and waved my arms and said heeee and haaaa like good Dr Sun and shook my chi like a holy roller like previous Charlie had shown me how and called and called and called without saying any words out loud but just feeling my heart squeeze the names out like the end of the toothpaste tube so tight it almost hurt but didn't quite. I called on Green Tara and White Tara and Medicine Buddha *Sanje Menla* and anyone big who might be listening. And then I was re-minded

287

of when I asked Rinpoche if it is OK to call for help in case they might be busy or it was not polite or anything and he smiled kindness itself and said "Rinchen they ARE help." And I checked also that they could be helping me and still be there for anyone else if they needed them because I wouldn't want to stop them being there for babies and dogs and hospitals or anything and he explained that they can be many places at once. So that was all right then. So I called.

And Charlie began to shake and shake on the inside and outside both, like a mad waterfall and then like a river and then maybe like a hurricane like I saw on TV and he started to cry like an ambulance so I stopped saying heeee and haaaa and sat close by him to be sure he was warm because he wasn't wrapped up or dressed sensibly or anything. And Murray knew to come close and hold him in his arms like a little boy and after a while a long long while the crying got soft like rain on the ocean when it's falling back to being just ocean and Murray helped Charlie to go inside the house because it is warm and soft there and put him to sleep on the big squashy sofa with a huge plump duvet from Mum's bed. And then the Following Cat knew to come also and we snuggled down beside him and showed him how to sleep by pretending to. And he did.

Then Murray said we could leave him with the cat and he must sleep now. And he took me into the kitchen and said nice Murray things and made me drink a very sweet hot drink and made me waffles with maple syrup and banana and sang me a song about a blackbird in the middle of the night waiting for a moment and was very very kind, and safe as safe can be.

A little bit later on, when almost all the syrup was gone and I licked the plate with my finger because otherwise the Following Cat might see it with his nose and eat it and it's not good for cats to have sugar, Mum came home. She had huge bunches of flowers from a shop which is strange because there are lots of flowers in the garden but she said these were a special occasion and a celebration. Murray sat her down carefully and said kind things to her because she was smiling and happy but with blue round her eyes from not being asleep in the night, and he told her about Charlie and not at all to worry and that it was done and dusted and that everything's gonna be all right. And she knew he was speaking the truth and cried one green tear and one white tear but mostly didn't have to because he said it all so well and so clear. And she hugged me and said I'd done a good job and I said that really it was Green Tara and White Tara and Medicine Buddha and Murray and Joel and Dr Sun teaching me by showing me and Rinpoche and the Following Cat who was at a distance. And she said what a team and held me very close.

A little bit later, when Murray had given Mum some waffles too only without syrup and banana and with honey and almonds and she was yawning and getting ready to have a snooze, we heard Charlie's voice coming from the music room so we knew he had woken up. It was a big boomy voice like people make in the street when they talk into their mobile phones and tell you all about themselves. And we all looked at each other a bit surprised because Charlie doesn't use his mobile phone any more.

—Oh Rinchen, said my Mum, Oh Rinchen—listen to Charlie. He's calling Joel.

And he was doing.

October 2004

Charlie: journal

Rinpoche is coming

So here we are. Ready and waiting.

Three weeks ago, my precious little friend had come running up the stairs to tell me her good news as soon as she heard me getting up. Her face a thing of joy and wonder. And beauty. Ah. Such beauty.

—Charlie, Charlie, Rinpoche is coming!

—Really, dearest?

—Yes Charlie, Mum just heard on the telephone, he is coming to England to give teachings and initiations in London, and he is going to come and stay with us!

—That's nice, dear.

—Nice! Nice! This is better than nice! This is enormous! Stop thinking about Shakespeare, Charlie, this is very important!

—Shakespeare is important maybe too.

—Maybe, maybe, you will explain this maybe, but later; Rinpoche is alive and answers questions.

—OK, true. Tell me about him, then, Rinchen.

—Well. Rinpoche means precious one. Like my name, same thing: precious. But for me it is just a nice name, for him it is what we call people who are special teachers. He is a precious master who can help us to be free and happy.

—He can do that?

—Of course he can do that, that is *everything he does*. You will see, Charlie, you will see. You must be very respectful because he is very high in Tibetan tradition. It is like having a king come to visit, Charlie, we must clean the house and wear nice clothes and—

—And be on our best behaviour?

—Well no, he likes worst behaviour, too. He likes to laugh. You will see.

—I like to laugh too, or I used to, anyway.

—You should laugh more, now, Charlie, it is time to laugh more. Rinpoche will make you laugh, he does that. This is the most important thing that has happened to you in your whole life, Charlie; don't mess it up!

It was lovely to see her so excited. She is finding, more and more, her Tibetan roots, and obviously having someone who is respected and important in Tibetan circles come to stay is wonderful for her. For me, I'm not so sure. I've never been one for religion, it just hasn't featured in my life: we are born, we die, and in the middle there is a song and dance act. Sing and dance as well as you can, because when you stop dancing you die. As I nearly did. I've never had much to do with Hattie's connection with Tibetan Buddhism, or really understood it. Whatever she does is fine by me, admirable, perfect, because it is Hattie; but, for myself, I am over by the mirror, perfecting my *pliés*, my dears.

Charlie: journal

Priest king

The house was immaculate: Hattie had gathered a small army of helpers and they had turned the whole place bewilderingly upside down, so what had been a comfortable rambling mansion became a somewhat less comfortable iridescently clean rambling mansion.

—Er, Hattie, I had ventured at one point, and she silenced me with a look.

—Respect, Charles, she said: it's about respect.

So there we were, lined up, waiting for the priest in our best frocks; Hattie a swirl of colours, Rinchen in her Tibetan outfit, which I had never seen before, long skirt, bright colours, strings of beads in her hair, and me in a nice suit speedily imported the previous evening.

I have met various bits of royalty, from time to time, and more or less knew the routine. Respect, yes, sternly upright (the Englishman should *not* bow below the shoulders, my Grandfather said, and I believed him); firm handshake and polite small talk, resist the temptation to send the whole thing up, or indeed blow it sky high. I was quite pleased to notice that temptation arising again, by the way, I am becoming almost human, I thought, and then repressed it.

So there we were in a line, Hattie first, then me as the token paterfamilias I guess, then Murray, then Rinchen, then the Following Cat.

Up swept a moderately posh car. I maintained the posture, bolt upright, hands behind back, credit to my upbringing, and noticed I was somewhat alone in this, because everyone else was bent double, hands together in prayer position. We are supposed to pray to this guy? And then I noticed that everyone was also grinning like idiots, on their faces the pure anticipation of joy. Hattie, I thought rather desperately, Hattie, my truly unusual friend, what exactly is happening here? And then out he came.

A big man. Maroon robes over a bright yellow shirt. Sensible solid shoes. Bent over towards us, hands in the praying posture (he prays to us? What?) and then he is in front of Hattie. She curtseys *(Hattie?)* and gives him a white scarf, which he loops round her neck, and then takes her hands, and, very gently, very delicately, quite slowly, bumps his forehead against hers. At which point Hattie goes slightly cross-eyed and totters a little. He holds her hands to make sure she's OK, then says something quietly, and moves on to me.

Me standing there like a beanpole, not knowing what the hell was happening; and he stood there, in front of me, looking up (though he's as tall as I am), and. And. He took my hand, to shake it, and clasped it with his other hand too, and smiled, and said, quietly, Charlee, and looked at me. I had my stiff actor's face on, and he looked right through it, and the touch of his hands was an electric shock, and he showed me, as if giving a beautiful simple gift, what kindness was actually like. My eyes suddenly overflowed with tears, and he smiled, and said Charlee, quietly, and moved on. And I just stood there, looking straight ahead of me, tears on my cheeks, hearing squeals of joy from Rinchen on my left as he picked her up and kissed her, me still looking straight ahead, gobsmacked, visited by bliss.

The next thing I knew was Murray's arm round my shoulder, and his voice rumbling:

—Come on Charles, a nice cup of tea is what you need; it's a bit odd, the first time, isn't it? And he led me into the house.

Charlie, Murray

What was that?

—Er, Murray, er, what *was* that?

—What was what?

—That thing that he did.

—Charles, you are not making a lot of sense here. What thing that who did?

—Rinpoche. When he zapped me.

—Oh, that was the bliss. Nice, isn't it? Very good that you picked it up: it takes two, you know.

—Murray, what are you talking about?

—All right, back to basics. Rinpoche is a very advanced practitioner of Tibetan Tantric Buddhism. He's spent many years in solitary meditation in an unheated cave high up in the frozen mountains. What he was doing up there was learning control of the mind. Those that know say he became very good at it. OK so far?

—Er, I guess.

—Right. Stay with it. Now: if you achieve a certain level of realisation you are able to directly cognise the inherent emptiness of categorisation.

—Murray!

—Sorry. What it means is: all designations are relative. Obviously. You are tall compared to Hattie, but not compared to me. You do not have an inherent quality of tallness: you are empty of that quality. Right?

—I guess.

—Well, truly and fully considered all categories are equally empty. Including, and especially, Charleyness and Murrayness and Rinpocheness.

—Wait a minute. I exist, God damn it. Descartes—

—Was a dickhead. Your sense of Charleyness is actually a loose con-glomeration of sense impressions, mental states, and externally applied illusions. A makeshift. A *bricolage.* Don't interrupt. Now, it's one thing to realise that intellectually, anyone can do that; but to experience it directly, to fully know it, is something else again. To be able to do so is rare and precious. It's called experiencing emptiness, or *sunyata,* and a by-prod-uct of that realisation is what is known as bliss. It's hard work being you, Charlie, as you surely know, and if you could take a holiday it would be very nice. Rinpoche can take that holiday, and when he is in that state, if you have a certain level of sensitivity you can pick up on the experience like tuning in to a broadcast, and this is beyond nice.

—And that's what it was?

—That's what it was. And those who have it, don't talk about it. They say to talk about it dilutes it. But if they think you are very advanced, and very precious, they give you the head bump, which you'll have to ask Hat-tie about, because I don't understand it. What he does with me, before you ask, is, usually, he grabs my sideburns and shakes them, laughing like a drain: Tibetans think sideburns are hilarious. Actually Tibetans think a lot of things are hilarious, it's one of their traits. One of the high teachers said once, enlightenment is like having a sense of humour. Is that enough for now?

—Yes, Murray, thank you, that's enough for now.

Hattie: journal

An ocean of joy

It's wonderful having Rinpoche here. Such a huge, warm, reliable presence. How can I describe it? It's as if the sun were shining constantly. Everyone expands. It's a feeling of being able to relax and luxuriate in lovingkind-ness and dance lightly through the play of the everyday.

Thank heavens Murray is here. He understands completely.

Many of the devotees are confused, poor things. They arrive with what Rinchen calls their 'going to church' faces and are full of the effort of do-ing being good and trying to be some sanitised Western version of pure and holy. So solemn. So leaden. Don't they see? Don't they get it?

Would it, I wonder, be a good idea to shake them? Probably not. But I wonder if some mischief is in order? Divine mischief. I wish Charlie were available for his playful, disruptive part. Then we could move and shake to our hearts' content. That would be good—some moving and shaking. And some rich, rolling, golden laughter.

Rinpoche laughs like an ocean of joy.

Rinchen, visitor

A busy woman

—Slugs.

—Pardon?

—Slugs.

—Who are you?

—I'm Rinchen. I live here. Who are you please?

—I've come to see Rinpoche. I have an appointment. I'm seeing Rinpoche at 11.15.

—But you trod on slugs. On the path.

—So?

—So? SO? Are you mad?

—Look, little girl, I'm a busy woman. I've driven a long way. There was traffic. I'm tired. I'm here to see my teacher. I need to come in.

—But the slugs are squished. They're dead.

—Well. Yes, I'm sorry about that. I wasn't looking where I was walking. I've got problems. Issues.

—You think *you've* got problems? What about the slugs?

Rinchen, Jacqui

You understand lots

—Hello.

—Hello, may I come in?

—Have you come to see Rinpoche?

—Yes, I have. Thank you.

—You're welcome. Do you want some tea or something?

—That would be lovely. I'd love a cup of hot water.

—OK. I'll get it.

—Thank you.

—Are you the lady with the voice?

—The voice?

—Yes, the nice phone voice—we spoke yesterday.

—Well, I did call yesterday. And I spoke to a person who sounded a lot like you. Only taller.

—Yes, That's me. I can sound quite tall when I want to.

—And when is that?

—When I'm doing things for Rinpoche. I was being his PA yesterday.

—Oh I see. Yes, that must require a certain sort of height.

—It does.

—Do you think I should be a bit taller to see Rinpoche?

—Oh no. you're perfect the way you are—and anyway, Rinpoche doesn't mind. It's just me—I like to do things properly.

—Me too, I like to do things properly.

—Well, you could be taller if it would make you happier.

—Do you know, I think it might. I'll give it a try and see.

—Yes. That's a good idea. Try it and see. What's your name?

—My name's Jacqui. My friends call me Jac.

—That's a good name. I used to be called Charly.

—Did you?

—Yes, then real Charlie needed his name back. So I gave it back.

—And did that help?

—I think so. You understand lots, don't you, Jac?

—I hope so, used-to-be-Charly. I do hope so.

297

Rinchen: blog

Going for a song

So I was sitting quietly in my room and imagining the cat and listening to an early Crazy Wisdom Lady song on my computer and there was a knock and Mum came in and looked startled.

—That's Joel on guitar, she said.

—Yes it is, I said.

—How did you get *hold* of that? That's the unbelievable version of *Jerusalem* that he did in our first open air concert!

—Yes, Mum, I know.

—But we could never remember how he did it, it was a one-off, lost forever!

—I think someone in the audience must have had a tape-recorder, Mum.

—So are you playing a tape?

—No Mum. I found it on the internet. Crazy Wisdom Lady is all over the internet.

—Really?

—Yes, really and very much. Lots of early tapes, bootlegs, and so on.

—But how do they get on the internet?

Mum is not very good with electricity. I think she thinks it's unlikely. She is more on the magic side of things.

I told her about file sharing and MP3 compression and Napster and all of those things. She looked like, *What?*

—Show me, she said.

So I booted up a file sharing program and typed in crazy wisdom lady and hit return and the internet thought about it and then all the titles started scrolling down, and down, and down, and she gasped.

—Look at that, she said, I only wrote that last week!

—Did you sing it in your guest appearance at Jon's concert on Saturday?

—Yes, but—

—Someone must have had a tape recorder, Mum.

—Where is it now, then?

—Well, that version is in Minnesota, Mum, but the true answer is, everywhere. Because the internet is everywhere.

—And you can play that?

I downloaded it, which took one minute and 32 seconds, and clicked on play. Out through the speakers it came. The look on her face was quite funny.

—So all our early stuff, and the new stuff, is kind of floating about everywhere for anyone to listen to?

—Pretty much, yes.

—How much does it cost? Is someone making money out of our music?

—Nothing and nobody, Mum. It's, like, going for a song.

—Going for a song? She had her songwriting face on.

—Yes, I said, going for a song.

Rinchen: blog

Pete the Geek

So we went downstairs and she made a cup of tea and Murray was there peeling potatoes very very beautifully, as he does, and we talked.

—So I could write a song and it could go on the internet and be everywhere? said Mum.

—It could, easily, said Murray. But the trouble with the file sharing setup is that it's unreliable and a bit complicated and you get incomplete downloads and so on. It's messy.

—Why?

—Well, because it's illegal. The record companies are not happy about it, as you can imagine. What you really need is your own server, then you could have a website and control the quality and make it easy for everyone to have access to your music—if that's what you want.

—Can you set it up?

—Me? No. Pete can, though, Pete the Geek. Easily. He's a good designer, too. He'd make you a nice website, and you could run it on one of his servers, he's got plenty of space.

—What's he like?

—Like a geek. But he's also a serious Buddhist; you have to catch him when he's not in retreat. He made a vast amount of money from a couple of early patents, and now he mostly plays with computers and does Dharma practice.

—Better and better.

—I'll talk to him.

—Murray, that would be wonderful. Thank you.

Pete, Murray

Hmm

—Speak.

—For Christ's sake Peter, why can't you answer the phone like a normal human being?

—Hi Murray, what can I do for you?

—It's about Hattie Tattersall.

—*The* Hattie Tattersall? That mega-rich retired pop star you hang out with?

—The one and only. She needs a website.

—Everyone needs a website.

—She needs someone good to set it up for her and host it and maintain it.

—And you want me to do the work?

—Yes please.

—No.

—Why not?

—There are plenty of people out there who'll take her money. Some of them even know how to code a little.

—She's a Buddhist, Pete.

—What kind of Buddhist?

—What is this, the Inquisition? She's a personal student of Wangchuk Namjal Rinpoche and does a lot of serious practice.

—Hmm.

—Look, this is a good thing, Pete; she wants to give her music away. Open source. Free the information. For the benefit of all beings.

—Hmm.

—OK, you drive a hard bargain; how about if she came to see you, to talk about it? Tomorrow?

—Hmm. OK.

Pete, Murray

Musical blog

—Speak.

—No, you speak.

—Hi Murray.

—Tell me what you thought of Hattie.

—I'm in love.

—Makes sense.

—You know she came with a suitcase? Full of tapes?

—Yes.

—Murray, she played me some of the tapes.

—Yes. And?

—Fuck.

—Good, were they?

—They were: *astonishing*. And she's got shelfloads of them, she says. One tape, one song, every two or three days, since the early eighties. Some guy called Mark set her up a very user-friendly recording system, and the tapes are really rather high quality.

—So you'll do the website?

—Obviously.

—Any good ideas?

—One or two.

—Do I have to drag them out of you?

—We're going to digitise her recording setup, so she can record seam-lessly straight into the computer. And put it all on the website; kind of like a musical blog.

—Quite cool.

—Yes. Plus we'll pull in copies of all of the bootlegs and bits and pieces that are floating around in cyberspace, tidy them up, and set them out so that anyone can download authoritative copies. And catalogue and digitise all of the tapes, and put them up, gradually, also. There's a big fan base, there will be people who would adore to do the work. Build up a complete sound picture of the band's history.

—Including the albums? Aren't there copyright problems?

—No, that's the beauty of it; when the band was becoming famous they refused to make albums for a long time, so the record companies got very very hungry; and when they signed a contract the band hired some seriously fierce lawyers; they have legendary freedom to do what they like with the music. Awesome, it is, their recording contract.

—All of this is very nice, isn't it?

—It is, Murray, it is. Very nice.

—Right. It's not enough, is it?

—Not yet. No.

Hattie, Joel

Training

—Oh Joel, Joel, sometimes I can't bear it that you died.

—No.

—I mean, talking to you like this is wonderful, but it's not the same.

—No.

—And you could be a projection, anyway, couldn't you?

—I could. Of course, I always was. But yes, I could.

—And then Dad died, and Charlie nearly died, and now Morris is dead, that big kind man.

—And your mother, and Fritz the kitten, and Manny Cohen, my uncle Manny whom I never met.

—Yes, yes.

—And the Lady and the Parfait, in the twelfth century, burned at the stake.

—Oh, yes.

—In fact pretty much everyone in the twelfth century is dead, come to think.

—Oh, Joel.

—And Charlie is dead and Rinchen is dead—

—No they're not!

—They're dying, Hattie, and so are you, dying all the time.

—I can't bear it. It is not supportable.

—Yes it is; you just need practice, that's all.

—Practice?

—Yes, training courses. How to die. How to sit with the dying. That sort of thing. You should organise it.

—Me?

—Who else? You're famous, influential, photogenic, rich, and bloody intelligent. Who else?

—And I'm going to have a website…

—Exactly.

—I'll talk to Pete the Geek. I'm sure he'll go for it. It could be wonderful…

—I think the dead will be very grateful, Hattie.

Pete, Hattie

Grateful

—Speak.

—Hey, Pete.

—Hattie. How nice.

—Listen, Pete, that website idea, the free songs and music blog and so on.

—Yes.

—It needs to go up a level, doesn't it?

—It does.

—What about death?

—Death?

—Death. I want to set up training courses, where you can learn how to die, learn how to sit with the dying, that sort of thing.

—Death. Free songs and death.

—Yes. Don't you think it's a great idea?

—Sex is more popular.

—Doesn't last as long, though, does it?

—Not in my experience, no. Plenty of scope for humour, then?

—Absolutely.

—It's a design challenge. Free songs and death.

—You can do it.

—Yes, I think I can.

—Think of the benefit to sentient beings!

—I'm sure the dead will be very grateful.

—I've heard that one before, Pete.

Rinchen, Charlie

Death and dying

—Mum's going to put her music online Charlie, have you heard?

—Murray told me something about it, yes.

—There's a man called Pete who says speak because he's a genius, he's going to do it.

—Right.

—So she's going to give away the back catalogue.

—Brilliant. Never liked that record company. They'll be really unhappy.

—And it's going to be about death.

—About *what?*

—Death. She wants to set up an organisation to help people who are dying, and to help people who help people, she is going to sort death out.

—Christ!

—Pardon?

—Er, sorry, I was a bit surprised.

—Yes it is surprising isn't it. Are you going to help?

—No, Rinchen, I don't think I can do that.

—Why ever not? You set up the clowns' hospital thingy, didn't you? That was fairly awesome. And you did all that work with dying children.

—Well the problem is that that is what made me ill, really, and I'm a bit frightened of going back there.

—Why is that, Charlie?

—It's because I got into a space where if I looked out, I saw nothing but suffering, and the worst suffering of all, which is death. And if I looked in, I saw—nothing. I was empty, insubstantial, a machine with no ghost, living in a nightmare landscape, bones and dust. And all of my acting and clowning was just a device to hide that fact, that landscape, from me. So I became a broken toy. I let death in from the outside, because there was nothing inside to stop it. Oh God Rinchen I'm sorry, don't listen, I'm just talking to myself, I'm so sorry.

—No Charlie it's OK, really, you sound like Rinpoche.

—I *what?* Like *Rinpoche?*

—Yes, Charlie, he says those things.

—But he's a saint! He's a holy man, a priest!

—What does that mean?

—Er, er, he has glad kindness and certainty and meditative calm and, and, he's *happy,* damn it!

—Yes damn it Charlie he is all those things and much more. And yester-day in his teachings which I went to he said, first, that the world is full of suffering, every part of it, every single atom and bit of it, terrible suffering, yes. That's the first thing, he said. And he said also that there is no self. If you look inside, he said, you can't find it, however hard you look; that's exactly what he said.

—But he's happy! He smiles!

—Yes, that's *why* he smiles Charlie, that's the whole point, I think.

—I don't understand.

—When you talk to him, you will understand. Listen, Charlie, here is something I learned. You can't be dead in Tibetan.

—Can't you?

—No. You can be dying, in fact you are, everyone is all the time, and of course there are corpses and so on, but you can't be dead. You are just a stage.

—A stage?

—Yes, you are just a stage you are going through.

—All the world's a stage?

—Yes, brilliant, Charlie, that's exactly right.

—Shakespeare.

—Ah, see, the best!

—All the world's a stage,
And all the men and women merely players:
They have their exits and their entrances;
And one man in his time plays many parts.

—Yes exactly Charlie, that's just what Rinpoche says. Shakespeare was an actor, wasn't he?

—Yes, he was.

—So he knows. Acting is really good, you see, because actors *know* the world's a stage.

—Rinchen you have truly and totally baffled me. I am bewitched, bothered, and bewildered.

—Rinpoche will explain, Charlie. It will be absolutely fine.

Rinchen, Hattie

Necklace

—Mum?

—Yes sweetheart?

—What is that necklace you always wear?

—Do you like it? It's my Gingerbread Pig. Grandad gave it to me a long time ago.

—What's a Gingerbread Pig?

—What do you think it might be?

—I need to think about it, I think.

—Think on, precious. Think on.

Rinchen, Hattie

Cat walk

—Mum?

—Yes sweetheart?

—How long ago? How long ago did Grandad give you your Gingerbread Pig?

—When I was littler than you, precious.

—No, I mean precisely how long?

—Is precisely a new word?

—Newish. Charlie gave it me. Along with precision and precise. It's for the dance we're doing. And the cat walk.

—Cat walk?

—Yes, we followed the Following Cat. Charlie said I had to do copy cat precisely.

—And then?

—Then I knew what it felt like being the Following Cat. I fuzzy knew before, but now I know precisely.

—And how does it feel?

—Warmhappy slowflow mellow then arrowjump swoosh hit target yeah!

Actually.

—That's pretty precise.

—Yes. It is actually. Very pretty. But how long ago?

—Well, it was September, just before I went to school for the first time, so it was precisely, um, 49 years and 1 month ago.

—So how old were you precisely?

—I was precisely four and a half.

—Do you know how a Gingerbread Pig feels?

—Oh yes. Yes I do.

—So tell me how?

—Ask Charlie to read you his story about Grandad and me when I was four and a half precisely, and then you can find out for yourself.

—OK. That's cool.

Rinchen, Joel

Asking Rinpoche

—Joel?

—*Guten tag.*

—Yes it is isn't it. Especially today.

—Why today especially?

—Because today Simon is coming to translate for Rinpoche when his students come to see him with their questions, and he's said that me and the Following Cat can sit and listen.

—Hey—that's truly special.

—Yes, it is, isn't it?

—And do you have anything to ask him yourself?

—I ask him stuff all the time. He tells me stuff all the time. And sometimes he asks me things.

—I know, precious.

—How do you know, Joel?

—He asks me things too.

—What sort of things, Joel?

—Why not ask him precious?

—OK Joel, that's a Rinpoche sort of thing to do.

Rinchen: blog

Translating Rinpoche

Hey blog. Today was a really special day. Again. I got to sit next to Rinpoche the whole day. The whole total day. We had tea and little cakes and lunch and supper and did pujas and sitting practice and everything. He was very happy. He is always happy though I think. Even when he is sad. Me and the Following Cat, we were happy too.

And in the afternoon, Simon came and sat next to Rinpoche too—only lower down like me—which is more comfortable. Obviously. And people came and asked their questions and Simon translated in funny Tibetan that made Rinpoche laugh a lot, which was just as well because the people were very very serious. They had their listening to the poet while she's reading you her poem faces (Charlie says that) on a lot of the time. Except the nice lady Jac. She had a smiley face and a totally mellow laugh. Mellow's a good word, isn't it? Murray told me that one. Mellow yellow he said. He was singing about saffron which is a colour as well as a girl's name. So I asked him if he had a new girlfriend and he said he hadn't, temporarily. I asked him if he was in love and he said love was a field and he definitely was in it because Rinpoche is here.

At the end of the day I asked Simon to ask Rinpoche a precise question please because my Tibetan is a still a bit fuzzy. Simon said his was fuzzy too, and we laughed a lot and had to stop and explain to Rinpoche what fuzzy meant. He likes new words like me. He likes 'temporarily' a lot. He says everything is temporarily.

But then I got to ask my question: Rinpoche, how come when different people ask the same question you give them different answers? He gave Simon a look and Simon gave him a look which would have been awesome except the Following Cat made Simon sneeze a lot which made Rinpoche laugh a lot which made me laugh a lot. And then Rinpoche said long long bits of Tibetan even though Tibetan is sometimes very short bits really I think. And Simon said that western people think there are only right and wrong answers to questions but if you're helping people on their way in the Dharma you have to listen very precisely to who is asking the question. Not the who that they think they are. And not the Buddha who—who isn't. But the who who is ready for the next instruction.

So then I asked if I could ask more questions and Rinpoche clapped his hands and said 'Yes yes questions good questions good.' So I asked what I should say to people when they don't understand why Rinpoche has said different answers to same questions, and they think he doesn't have the right answer. And he said not to worry, people like to make unnecessary suffering that way, temporarily, till they decide to stop making unnecessary suffering. But I said I didn't like it when they didn't get it, how totally awesome he is. And when he understood my question which took him and Simon quite a bit of fuzzy Tibetan I think, he laughed bigger and more and lots and plenty and said it doesn't matter what people think of him. It's not personal, said Simon, though that's not quite what Rinpoche said I think. Simon said Rinpoche doesn't take it personally. He knows what he knows, and it's OK that they don't totally get it yet. Oh I said. He's a Gingerbread Pig like Mum!

And I tried to tell Simon the story so he could tell Rinpoche, but I got confused in the middle so we decided that Simon could read Charlie's written down story and then tell Rinpoche. Simon said he likes a challenge, he is totally kind. And then we had to explain challenge to Rinpoche. Him too. He likes a challenge. Obviously.

Rinchen, Murray

Gingerbread

—Excuse me Murray. Are you busy?

—Just cooking Rinchen. Happy to stop and talk to you. What can I do for you ma'am?

—Do you know how to cook gingerbread Murray?

—Cake or biscuits?

—Biscuits. Definitely.

—Yes. I know how to do that. Do you want me to make you some?

—Thank you, Murray, but actually could you show me how to actually?

—Of course I could. Do you have a window in your diary?

—I don't have a diary, Murray.

—Then we must get you one.

—Why?

—Because then you could have windows in it.

—Like on the computer?

—More like in a house.

—OK. And making gingerbread? Biscuits.

—This afternoon maybe? Around 3.30?

—I'll be here, Murray. I'll be here thank you.

Rinchen, Charlie

Jelly babies

—Hello Charlie.

—Hello Rinchen. Have you been out?

—Yes. Me and Murray took Rinpoche to see Henley.

—Did you have a nice time?

—Yes thank you Charlie. We had ice cream and sat by the river and watched lots of people in boats and caught the sun.

—So you have.

—And we saw Annabel Atkinson and her Mum and her little brother Jeremy and he was eating jelly babies which made Rinpoche a bit sad.

—Really? Why so?

—Well, he just saw a little boy biting the head off another little boy and that made him sad. Obviously.

—Yes. It would do. You're right. That is obvious. Thank you.

—That's a pleasure Charlie.

—I remember once, a long time ago, your Mum told me something that should have been obvious about Guy Fawkes.

—But it wasn't?

—No. It really wasn't. Not till she explained it to me. Like you just did.

—I think you are a who who is ready for the next instruction Charlie.

—Do you precious?

—Definitely.

—What should I do? Tell me.

—Ask Joel. Ask Rinpoche. Ask the Buddha who. Who isn't, by the way.

—Isn't?

—Definitely. Definitely isn't. Is not.

Rinchen, Murray

Dilemma

—Murray, I have a problem. A dilemma

—Hey, that's a good word.

—Yes, isn't it. I learned it from that nice lady.

—Jac?

—Yes. That one.

—Well, what is your dilemma? How can I help you with your dilemma, my friend?

—I like it that you're my friend, Murray.

—Me too. Me very sincerely too.

—Sincerely like in yours?

—Absolutely. Absolutely yours.

—OK. That's cool. Can I tell you my dilemma now?

—Now that yours sincerely is absolutely clear and sorted, go ahead.

—Well, you know the story of the Gingerbread Pig?

—I know a story about a gingerbread man.

—OK well there's this story about a Gingerbread Pig that Grandad told Mum when she was four and a half precisely and Charlie wrote it on his computer to be like a play and tonight after supper and puja Simon is going to put it into Tibetan so that Rinpoche can get to hear it. Are you OK so far?

—I'm following you so far.

—So I thought I could make—we could make—some Gingerbread Pigs for everyone to eat after they'd heard the story.

—Good idea.

—Yes, but.

—Yes but what?

—When we were in Henley this morning, Rinpoche got sad temporarily because he saw Jeremy Atkinson biting the heads off jelly babies. I don't want him to be sad about the Gingerbread Pigs.

—Ah. I understand. But he wasn't sad about the jelly babies, sweetheart. He was sad about Jeremy.

—Because?

—Because he wasn't aware of what he was doing. Too little.

—But they aren't really babies, Murray.

—But to Jeremy in his littleness they are. And he's being unkind to them.

—This is a bit confusing excuse me Murray.

—Yes it is a bit.

—I think I have to go away and think about it I think.

—OK sweetheart. Catch you later?

—Can't catch me Murray.

—Why not?

—I'm the Gingerbread Pig! Yeah.

Rinchen, Joel

The difference

—OK Joel, you have to help me out here.

—Always at your service. Your beck and call.

—Beck?

—Short for beckon, I reckon.

—OK. I don't think I know how to beckon.

—A new day a new skill.

—You're sounding like Charlie. Has he been calling a lot?

—Yes; I'm perfecting my role.

—Yes. That's it. That's truly cool. Can I tell you my dilemma now?

—Go ahead, *liebchen*.

—Well. Can I give Rinpoche a Gingerbread Pig to eat?

—Absolutely you can.

—Could I give Jeremy Atkinson who won't be here so it's a make believe question a Gingerbread Pig to eat?

—Not a good idea.

—What's the difference?

—The *difference* between Rinpoche and Jeremy *Atkinson*?

—Ooooooooh I totally get it. Thank you, Joel.

—There you go, *liebchen*.

—Am I yours sincerely?

—Shall I write you a letter?

—Would you say 'yours sincerely' at the end?

—If you wish.

—Yes I do wish.

—Your wish is granted.

—For the benefit of all sentient beings, obviously.

—Throughout space and time.

—Obviously Joel. Very precisely.

Murray: kitchen notice board

Gingerbread pig recipe

1 big chunk of butter (size of Rinchen's fist)
1 cup of sugar
1 nice egg
1 cup of light molasses (use the same cup!)
2 tbsp. vinegar

1 1/2 cup of flour

1 1/2 tsp. baking soda

1 tbsp. ginger. Fresh is good. Chop it fine. Dry is also ok.

1 tsp. cinnamon. Grind it with care and affection (and pestle and mortar).

1 tsp. cloves

1/2 tsp. salt. Sea salt is best.

In a big bowl, stroke and knead the sugar and butter until they are of one substance. You might warm the butter a little first, in a pan. Put all the other stuff in, and keep kneading, calmly and kindly, until they are one substance. Then lay it all out smooth on a floured breadboard, biscuit thickness. If you have a pig shaped biscuit cutter, use it to make pig shapes with. Otherwise, get creative with a small knife. Find interesting edible things to put on it to make it look nice, and pig-like. Whatever you have. Grease a biscuit tray with butter and pick the pigs up carefully one by one with a slice and put them on the tray. Bake them at 200 degrees until done. Decorate some more with whatever you have. Put on plate. Eat.

Rinchen, Charlie

That was me

—I've been for a walk with Rinpoche, Charlie.

—Have you? Isn't he teaching today?

—No. He's staying here today.

—Where did you go?

—I took him on a tour of the animals. He liked that a lot. So did they. Ayesha kissed him, a soft wet warm nuzzle kiss on his cheek, and he bumped her head ever so gently. And then he said lots of manis for them all.

—Manis?

—You know Charlie—the Chenrezig mantra—you know.

—Oh—*Om mane peme hung?*

—Right.

—Someone sang that to me when I was ill.

—That was me, Charlie.

—Was it, sweetheart?

—Yes.

—Thank you—I loved it.

—I know. I could see that.

—How could you?

—You did the little Buddha smile—not big cheesy grin or hey hey smile or being polite smile—little peaceful smile.

—Was I smiling at you?

—No—deep deep inside you were smiling.

—I thought it was an old old man who was singing to me. A very loving, all-knowing man. I smiled because he loved me. I was broken, and dishevelled and crying and hurting and seriously not my glittering loveable please the public Charlie-self, and yet I knew he loved me.

—He did.

—How do you know that sweetheart?

—That was me, Charlie.

Charlie: journal

A show

After he was installed with us in the best guest room, I saw very little of Rinpoche. Early every day Murray drove him into London to teach, usually with Hattie too; he mostly ate alone, for ritual reasons, Murray said—Murray did the cooking, as well as the chauffeur-bodyguard number, and was extremely happy. In the evening there was a steady trickle of devotees who came for audiences, carefully rationed by Hattie; she had several long talks with him, about I know not what, and Rinchen was in and out all the time, overflowing with joy.

And the former actor formerly known as Charlie didn't quite know what to do with himself. There was a strange high clean feeling in the house, even I could sense that, the joy, OK, the bliss; but I didn't know what to do about it. And, well, damn it, I was shy. Yes, dears, possibly for the first time in my life—well, they say an actor has to experience the gamut of emotions: OK, now I can handle all those great parts for shy people.

316

Then Hattie strode into my room, with her 'that's enough of that' look, and I steeled myself.

—OK, Charles, she said, enough's enough, I have a job for you. Oh no, not a *job,* I thought, not one of Hattie's *jobs.*

—You, my love, are going to do a show.

—A show?

—For Rinpoche.

—For Rinpoche, I said. Right. Er, what kind of a show?

—A panto. A really nice panto. Make him laugh.

—Hattie, I don't do that any more.

—Do not fuck with me, Charles Beaumont, you are going to do this, she said, you are a truly gifted clown and this man is my beloved teacher and you are bloody well going to make him laugh, OK?

—But I don't know anything about Tibetans, I said, I don't know what makes them laugh, I have no idea.

—Basil Fawlty, she said. The ego caught in its own ridiculous constructions. Embarrassment, farce, suffering, absurdity. Which makes you helpless with laughter because you recognise your own self importance, your own absurdity. That kind of thing.

—Kind of Don Quixote, I said.

—That's my boy, she said. Get to it. Oh, and mostly physical theatre, dearest, his English is a bit basic.

I got to it. A kind of kung fu spaghetti western, with music, and real spaghetti. Cooked, of course. We decided to keep it in-house, not import any stars. Murray was in, as a giant, with a Mexican accent and hat to match; Rinchen was Sancho in a rabbit suit; Simon turned out to be a really rather talented actor, as well as an extraordinary guitarist. Hattie sat at the piano and sang the narration and did some bit parts. And I looked for the character, inside myself.

And looked. In my previous life I could turn on the clown without thinking about it, or pick up a part and run with it without much introspection; but this was different. I felt the part grow, deepen, move.

On the night, it was electric. We had invited a whole lot of friends from the village, and they had a wonderful time. Simon brought his graceful partner Amanda, who understood the performance plan in an instant and swathed the stage with colour in her remarkable way. The beautiful twins were there, Hattie's dearest neighbours. It was a lovely bubbly audience.

The role, believe it or not, was more than I had ever done before. More. I could make them laugh, and then, still laughing, make them cry, I could feel it. It was big.

We did it mostly with kazoos, to get over the language problem. It's surprising, what you can do with a kazoo. Sometimes Hattie laughed so much she couldn't play the piano. Rinchen's timing and stage presence were immaculate. Rinpoche, on the front seat, a twin on each side of him, was helpless. I played it to him, orchestrating his laughter, pushing it, more and more. He was, I think, amazed.

He came up to me, afterwards, still laughing.

—Charlee, he said, Charlee; please come see me tomorrow morning OK? I bowed, and flattened my hands together, and he laughed some more, and went off, laughing.

And we all adjourned to the practice room for a bop. It was great. Some rock standards, some Crazy Wisdom Lady classics, Hattie's hands a blur on the piano, Murray slapping the drums, me doing a fairly competent bass line, and Simon having a wonderful time with lead guitar. And then, this happened.

We were well into 'Summertime Blues', and Hattie nodded at me to allow space for solos. I did some of my well rehearsed spontaneous bass riffs, Murray went nuts on the drum kit, Hattie was incomparable, as she is, and Simon stepped up and—launched into a Joel Cohen guitar solo. An authentic hand of God please don't stop I can't bear it Joel Cohen guitar solo, full of darkness and joy and the wailing wall. The dancers stopped, riveted, open mouthed. When he finished, everyone, us included, was applauding so much that we couldn't go on with the song, and had a bar break. During which I went up to him.

—Simon, I said, how did you learn to play like Joel Cohen?

—Who's Joel Cohen? he said.

Next day, I went to see Rinpoche.

Charlie, Murray

What am I going to say to him?

—So what am I going to say to him, Murray?

—I don't know, Charlie, it's kind of up to you.

—Well what do most people say to him?

—Depends. See, the thing is, this man is extremely learned, has memorised many many entire books and can cite them instantly, has been through the most sophisticated mind training exercise that, probably, any culture has ever devised, can answer with assurance and from first hand empirical knowledge pretty much any question you can ask him about the nature of mind, and—

—Yes, and?

—And has a rather basic grasp of English. In any case, we are so ignorant about the fundamentals of Buddhist psychology, as developed over a couple of thousand years of intensive study by numbers of very bright individuals spending whole lifetimes at it, in a language that has developed a highly specialised and extensive vocabulary for the sole purpose of dealing with states of mind, that we can't even really ask him an interesting question.

—Thank you for this, Murray, it is so encouraging.

—Any time, mate.

—What do you talk to him about, then?

—Oh, you know, cooking, the weather, not much traffic on the road today, that kind of thing.

—But isn't that a waste?

—It's hard for me to think, Charlie, of a more precious use of my time than just sitting in the same car as that man.

—Why?

—Charlie. Enough questions. Don't over-rehearse. Go in there and wing it. You'll be fine. If you blow it, don't worry, they say there's a lot to be said for the frog rebirth. Intellectually untroubling, you know. Virtually angst-free.

—Thank you, Murray.

—No worries, mate.

I stood outside the big white door and knocked, and, as instructed, went in. He was sitting cross-legged on one of Hattie's beautiful big white squashy sofas, beaming at me.

I prostrated, as instructed. This is quite a procedure. Hands in the prayer position, touch the forehead, throat, and heart, then bow and go all the way down, on your knees, bump the forehead on the floor, abject, in front of him. Then up again. Three times. God knows what my Grandfather would have said about that. Court-martialled me, I expect.

Slightly out of breath, I looked at him; he was still beaming. Squaawwwk, he said, suddenly, a very fair imitation of a kazoo. Squeeeek, I said back. And he laughed, and I laughed, and after that it was fine.

He's an actor, you know, I realised that. I know actors, I saw it in him. Not like any actor I have ever met or imagined, but an actor nonetheless. He knew me the way you know an audience, and gave me what I needed the way you deliver what the audience wants. Without much in the way of words. Breathtaking. Of course, that's me looking back, saying that; at the time I was spellbound.

Rinchen: blog

Backflips

This morning was a happy day. Maybe it was the happiest day.

I was sitting eating my cornflakes very carefully in order not to make a noise and Mum was sitting looking at a cup of coffee and Charlie was up with Rinpoche for a long time and Murray was making some toast. Then Murray said a Word, and we looked at him, and he was staring out of the window with a strange face.

—Murray, said Mum, what is it?

—Charlie, he said. On the lawn.

—What's he doing?

—Backflips.

—*Backflips?*

So we rushed and Mum lifted me up to see and there was Charlie on the big lawn, doing cartwheels then perfect beautiful backflips then more cart-wheels in a big circle on the lawn in the early morning, in the dewy grass, in his beautiful visiting Rinpoche suit, round and round and round.

And then he had to stop out of breath panting like a happy dog and lay on his back in the wet grass in the golden misty sunshine, arms stretched out staring up at the sky and he looked more happy than I have ever ever seen him, or maybe anyone, look.

So we rushed out with wet feet and Mum said

—Charlie Charlie what did he say to you? And Charlie laughed and laughed and panted some more and laughed and panted, so happy, then he sat up, and in a perfect Rinpoche voice he said:

—Make peoples laugh Charlee.

—That's it?

—That is it. That is absolutely it. Yes.

—Well what were you doing up there all this time?

—Mostly teaching him the kazoo. He was very impressed by the kazoo. He said 'western science very good squaaawk squaawwk.' And then he laughed and laughed, and so did I.

—Charlie, said Mum, you're back.

—Not just back, he said, I'm better than ever, and he sprang to his feet which is very hard to do and started singing a song about singing in the rain and kicking up sprays of water and Murray and Mum got up and joined in and I joined in too but I didn't know the words and we all got really really wet and I took the day off school because otherwise I might catch a chill from the wet and yes I think it was the happiest day of my life so far.